UCSMP Textbook Translations

Japanese Grade 7 Mathematics

Kunihiko Kodaira
Editor

UCSMP Textbook Translations

Japanese Grade 7 Mathematics

Kunihiko Kodaira
Editor

Translator
Hiromi Nagata

Translation Editor
George Fowler

The University of Chicago School Mathematics Project
1992

The University of Chicago School Mathematics Project

Zalman Usiskin, Director
Department of Education
The University of Chicago

Izaak Wirszup, Director
UCSMP Resource Development Component
Department of Mathematics
The University of Chicago

Financial support for the UCSMP Textbook Translations has been provided by the Amoco Foundation

New Mathematics 1, 2, and 3 for grades 7-9 were originally published 1984 in Japan by TOKYO SHOSEKI CO., LTD., Tokyo and approved by the Japanese Ministry of Education. Copyright © 1984 by Tokyo Shoseki Co., Ltd. All rights reserved.

English translation © 1992 by the University of Chicago
All rights reserved

ISBN 0-936745-53-3

TABLE OF CONTENTS

Textbook Series Preface

The University of Chicago School Mathematics Project

This textbook is part of a series of foreign mathematics texts that have been translated by the Resource Development Component of the University of Chicago School Mathematics Project (UCSMP). Established in 1983 with major funding from the Amoco Foundation, UCSMP has been since that time the nation's largest curriculum development and implementation project in school mathematics. The international focus of its resource component, together with the project's publication experience, makes UCSMP well suited to disseminate these remarkable materials.

The textbooks were originally translated to give U.S. educators and researchers a first-hand look at the content of mathematics instruction in educationally advanced countries. More specifically, they provided input for UCSMP as it developed new instructional strategies, textbooks, and materials of its own; the resource component's translations of over 40 outstanding foreign school mathematics publications, including texts, workbooks, and teacher aids, have been used in UCSMP–related research and experimentation and in the creation of innovative textbooks.

The resource component's translations include the entire Soviet curriculum (grades 1–10), standard Japanese texts for grades 7–11, and innovative elementary textbooks from Hungary and Bulgaria.

The content of Japan's compulsory national curriculum for grades 7–11 is made available for the first time in English, thanks in part to the generosity of the Japanese publisher, Tokyo Shoseki Company, Ltd., which provided the copyright permissions.

Japanese Secondary School Mathematics Textbooks

The achievement of Japanese elementary and secondary students gained world prominence largely as a result of their superb performance in the International Mathematics Studies conducted by the International Association for the Evaluation of Educational Achievement. The Second International Mathematics Study surveyed mathematics achievement in 24 countries in 1981-82 and released its findings in 1984. The results are recapitulated in a 1987 national report entitled "The Underachieving Curriculum: Assessing U.S. School Mathematics from an International Perspective" (A National Report on the Second International Mathematics Study, 1987).

Let us take a brief look at the schooling behind much of Japan's economic success. The Japanese school system consists of a six-year primary school, a three-year lower secondary school, and a three-year upper secondary school. The first nine grades are compulsory, and enrollment is now 99.99%. According to 1990 statistics, 95.1% of age-group children are enrolled in upper secondary school, and the dropout rate is 2.2%. In terms of achievement, a typical Japanese student graduates from secondary school with roughly four more years of education than an average American high school graduate. The level of mathematics training achieved by Japanese students can be inferred from the following data:

Japanese Grade 7 Mathematics (New Mathematics 1) explores integers, positive and negative numbers, letters and expressions, equations, functions and proportions, plane figures, and figures in space. Chapter headings in *Japanese Grade 8 Mathematics* include calculating expressions, inequalities, systems of equations, linear functions, parallel lines and congruent figures, parallelograms, similar figures, and organizing data. *Japanese Grade 9 Mathematics* covers square roots, polynomials, quadratic equations, functions, circles, figures and measurement, and probability and statistics. The material in these three grades (lower secondary school) is compulsory for all students.

The textbook *Japanese Grade 10 Mathematics* covers material that is compulsory. This course, which is completed by over 97% of all Japanese students, is taught four hours per week and comprises algebra (including quadratic functions, equations, and inequalities), trigonometric functions, and coordinate geometry.

Japanese Grade 11 General Mathematics is intended for the easier of the electives offered in that grade and is taken by about 40% of the students. It covers probability and statistics, vectors, exponential, logarithmic, and trigonometric functions, and differentiation and integration in an informal presentation.

The other 60% of students in grade 11 concurrently take two more extensive courses using the texts *Japanese Grade 11 Algebra and Geometry* and *Japanese Grade 11 Basic Analysis*. The first consists of fuller treatments of plane and solid coordinate geometry, vectors, and matrices. The second includes a more thorough treatment of trigonometry and an informal but quite extensive introduction to differential and integral calculus.

Some 25% of Japanese students continue with mathematics in grade 12. These students take an advanced course using the text *Probability and Statistics* and a second rigorous course with the text *Differential and Integral Calculus*.

One of the authors of these textbooks is Professor Hiroshi Fujita, who spoke at UCSMP's International Conferences on Mathematics Education in 1985, 1988, and 1991. Professor Fujita's paper on Japanese mathematics education appeared in *Developments in School Mathematics Education Around the World*, volume 1 (NCTM, 1987). The current school mathematics reform in Japan is described in the article "The Reform of Mathematics Education at the Upper Secondary School (USS) Level in Japan" by Professors Fujita, Tatsuro Miwa, and Jerry Becker in the proceedings of the Second International Conference, volume 2 of *Developments*.

Acknowledgments

It goes without saying that a publication project of this scope requires the commitment and cooperation of a broad network of institutions and individuals. In acknowledging their contributions, we would like first of all to express our deep appreciation to the Amoco Foundation. Without the Amoco Foundation's generous long-term support of the University of Chicago School Mathematics Project these books might never have been translated for use by the mathematics education community.

We are grateful to UCSMP Director Zalman Usiskin for his help and advice in making these valuable resources available to a wide audience at low cost. Robert Streit, Manager of the Resource Development Component, did an outstanding job coordinating the translation work and collaborating on the editing of most of the manuscripts. George Fowler, Steven R. Young, and Carolyn J. Ayers made a meticulous review of the translations, while Susan Chang and her technical staff at UCSMP handled the text entry and layout with great care and skill. We gratefully acknowledge the dedicated efforts of the translators and editors whose names appear on the title pages of these textbooks.

Izaak Wirszup, Director
UCSMP Resource Development Component

To the Student

The **Examples** are concrete examples to promote an understanding of the topic being studied. We have provided the subheadings of Approach and Solution as references for solving problems. A Solution outlined in a box is a model solution.

Problems are given to help you understand the topic under study. They also serve as preparation for upcoming topics. Furthermore, where additional study is necessary, **Drills** are provided.

Exercises are problems for reviewing the material in a certain section.

Chapter Exercises are provided as a review of the entire chapter and for practical application of the material. Part A treats the basic material, and Part B* treats the more advanced material.

In **Advanced Topics for Individual Study*** one can find further development of the topics in the chapter.

Review Exercises* are for summarizing and reviewing the material studied over the entire year. At intervals during your study **Computation Exercises*** will be provided. Doing them will improve your ability to calculate.

* Items marked with an asterisk are optional.

CHAPTER 1

INTEGERS

Numbers are being used all around us.

For example, when we say "The population of Japan is 120 million, and this is seventh largest in the world," the "120 million" is used to indicate the number of people, and the "7" expresses the order or rank compared with other countries in the world.

Can you think of other examples like those above, where numbers indicate quantities or orders of succession?

Train Boarding Information and Car Numbers

School Attendance Record

出　欠　表　4月1:

		丁	七	产	比点	匕点	油比	亨
1	1	20	19	39	39		1	
	2	19	18	37	36	1		
年	3	20	18	38	37	1		
	計	59	55	114	112	2	1	
2	1	20	18	38	37	1		

- Cars Produced in 1981 (ten of thousands)

1	Japan		697
2	USA		625
3	W. Ger.		358
4	France		261
5	USSR		135

THE NATURE OF INTEGERS

 Integers

Numbers that are used to express order and quantity, 1, 2, 3, 4, ..., are called **natural numbers**. Natural numbers combined with 0, as in 0, 1, 2, 3, 4, ..., are integers.

(Problem 1) We have decided to divide the 39 students in section 1 of a grade 1 class into groups. How many groups of 3 students can be formed? How many groups of 4 students can be formed?

There are two possibilities involving the division of integers, one with no remainder, as in 39 ÷ 3, and the other with a remainder, as in 39 ÷ 4.

In the case of 39 ÷ 4, the quotient is 9 and the remainder is 3. Among the numbers 39, 4, 9, and 3 there exists the following relation:

$$
\begin{array}{ccccccc}
39 & = & 4 & \times & 9 & + & 3 \\
\text{(dividend)} & = & \text{(divisor)} & \times & \text{(quotient)} & + & \text{(remainder)}
\end{array}
\qquad (1)
$$

The remainder is always less than the divisor. And when the remainder is 0, we say that the original number is evenly divisible.

(Problem 2) Calculate 39 ÷ 3 and 39 ÷ 5, and express the answers in the form of (1).

Divisors and Multiples

39 can be divided by 3. When, as in this example, integer a can be divided by integer b, we call b a divisor of a and a a multiple of b.

a divisor of 39

$39 = 3 \times 13$

a multiple of 3

Example 1 3 is a divisor of 39, and 39 is a multiple of 3.

Problem 3 6 can be expressed as 3 x 2. Write in the box below which is a 'divisor' and which is a 'multiple'.

(1) 6 is a ☐ of 3.   (2) 2 is a ☐ of 6.

Multiples of 3 other than 6 are:

    9, 12, 15, ...

without limit. These can be expressed as:

    3 x (integer).

3 and 0 are also multiples of 3.

    3 = 3 x 1,   0 = 3 x 0,

$$6 = 3 \times 2$$
$$9 = 3 \times 3$$
$$12 = 3 \times 4$$
$$15 = 3 \times 5$$
$$\vdots$$

Problem 4 In what form would you express multiples of 7?

Since any integer can be divided by 1, 1 is a divisor of all integers. Also, any integer multiplied by 0 equals 0, so 0 is a multiple of all integers.

Example 2 The divisors of 6 are 1, 2, 3, 6.
The multiples of 6 are 0, 6, 12, 18, ... without limit.

Problem 5 Give all the divisors of 8. Also, give all multiples of 8 which are less than or equal to 50.

Prime Numbers and Prime Factors

Prime Numbers

(**Problem 1**) There are 37 students in section 2 of a grade 1 class. Is it possible to divide those students into groups of equal numbers?

The only divisors of 37 are 1 and 37. As in the case of 37, those integers larger than 1 which have no divisors besides the number itself and 1 are called **prime numbers** (or primes).

(**Problem 2**) What are the divisors for the integers 1 through 10? Enter them into the chart at the right. Also, state the prime numbers which are less than or equal to 10.

Integer	Divisor		Integer	Divisor
1			6	
2			7	
3			8	
4			9	
5			10	

As we have discovered above, it can be said that prime numbers are integers which have only two divisors. 1 is not a prime number.

(**Problem 3**) Of 11, 21, 31, 41, and 51, which are the prime numbers?

Prime numbers can be found in the following manner:

(1)   Write down all integers through 60 that are greater than or equal to 2, as in the figure on the following page.

(2)   Circle 2, and cross out the larger multiples of 2.

(3)   Of the remaining numbers choose the smallest, 3, circle it, and cross out the larger multiples of 3.

(4)   As above, continue by circling the remaining smallest number and crossing out its multiples. The numbers which have been circled are the prime numbers.

The chart at the right depicts the situation after completing steps (1) and (2) and beginning step (3).

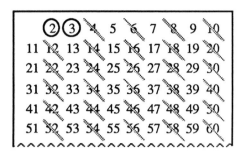

(Problem 4) Using this method, list all the prime numbers less than or equal to 60.

Factoring into Prime Factors

Let's think of expressing integers as products of smaller integers.

(Example 1) $12 = 2 \times 6$

If we express 6 in the form of a product, then the equation would look like this:

$12 = 2 \times 2 \times 3$

Since 2 and 3 are prime numbers, we cannot divide any further.

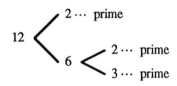

When we write $12 = 2 \times 6$, we say that the 2 and the 6 are **factors** of 12. In particular, if the factors are prime numbers we call them **prime factors**. Expressing integers as products of prime factors is called **factoring into prime factors**.

(Problem 5) Fill in the blanks below with numbers:

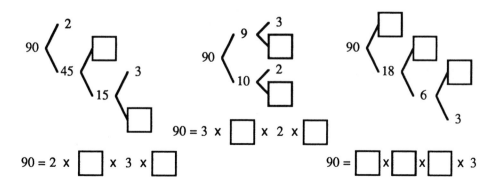

When factoring a number into primes, the results are the same regardless of the order of factoring.

Example 2   Let's factor 60 into prime factors:

(1)   Divide 60 by prime numbers, beginning with the smallest.

$$\begin{array}{r|r} 2 & 60 \\ \hline 2 & 30 \\ \hline 3 & 15 \\ \hline & 5 \end{array}$$

(2)   Write the products of those prime factors.

$60 = 2 \times 2 \times 3 \times 5$

Problem 6   Factor the following numbers into their prime factors:

(1)   66   (2)   68   (3)   72

To find all the divisors of a number, there is a method which uses factoring into prime factors.

Example 3   Since $165 = 3 \times 5 \times 11$, the divisors of 165 are the following numbers:

1	3×5	$= 15$
3	3×11	$= 33$
5 (prime factors)	5×11	$= 55$
11	$3 \times 5 \times 11$	$= 165$

(products of prime factors)

Problem 7   Find all the divisors of 42.

Powers

Problem 8 Factor 200 into its prime factors.

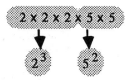

When a number is multiplied any number of times by itself, it is written in a certain form. For example, 5 x 5 is written 5^2. It is read as five to the **second power** or as the **square** of five. Again, 2 x 2 x 2 is written 2^3 and is read as either 2 to the **third power** or as the **cube** of 2. In this way, the number of times a number has been multiplied by itself is called the **power** of that number. The small number appearing to the upper right indicates how many times the number has been multiplied. It is called the **exponent**.

$$2^3 \longleftarrow \text{exponent}$$

Problem 9 Express each of the following using exponents:

(1) 4 x 4   (2) 10 x 10 x 10 x 10

(3) 3 x 3 x 5 x 5 x 5

Example 4 (1) $2^3 = 8, 3^2 = 9,$ $2^3 \times 3^2 = 8 \times 9 = 72$

(2) $2 \times 3^2 = 2 \times 9 = 18,$ $(2 \times 3)^2 = 6^2 = 36$

Problem 10 Calculate the following:

(1) 1^2 (2) 2^4 (3) 2×5^3

(4) $(2 \times 5)^3$ (5) $2^2 \times 3^3$

Example 5   2,375 can be shown as the following expression:

$$1,000 \times 2 + 100 \times 3 + 10 \times 7 + 1 \times 5$$

If we write this expression using powers of ten, it becomes the following:

$$2,375 = 10^3 \times 2 + 10^2 \times 3 + 10 \times 7 + 1 \times 5$$

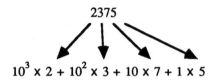

$$10^3 \times 2 + 10^2 \times 3 + 10 \times 7 + 1 \times 5$$

Problem 11   Express 3,457 and 8,205 using powers of ten.

Exercises

1   The following numbers are expressed in the form of (dividend) × (quotient) + (remainder). Place the appropriate numbers in the ☐ to make the equation correct.

(1) $44 = 5 \times \boxed{} + \boxed{}$ (2) $62 = \boxed{} \times 8 + \boxed{}$

2   Among the multiples of 13, find the one closest to 100.

3   Find all the divisors of the following numbers:

(1)   45   (2)   84   (3)   104

4   Factor the following numbers into their prime factors and express them using exponents:

(1)   54   (2)   147   (3)   336

2 COMMON DIVISORS AND COMMON MULTIPLES

Common Divisors and Greatest Common Divisors

When we group a collection of items, such as all the integers which are divisors of 6, we call this a set. Each item that belongs to the set is called an element.

For example, when we think about all the divisors of 12 as a group, the elements of this set are:

1, 2, 3, 4, 6, 12

We express the set of all the divisors of 12 by writing:

{1, 2, 3, 4, 6, 12}

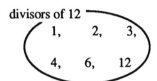

divisors of 12

1, 2, 3,

4, 6, 12

In the same way, the set of all the divisors of 18 is expressed:

{1, 2, 3, 6, 9, 18}

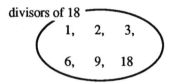

divisors of 18

1, 2, 3,

6, 9, 18

Problem 1 List all the elements which are common to both the set of all divisors of 12 and the set of all divisors of 18.

The divisors common to any integers are the common divisors of these numbers. This you learned in elementary school.

If we let the set of all the divisors of 12 be A and the set of all the divisors of 18 be B so that

A = {1, 2, 3, 4, 6, 12}

B = {1, 2, 3, 6, 9, 18}

then the set of all the elements common to A and B is

{1, 2, 3, 6},

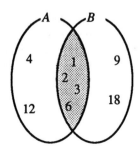

and this is the set of all the common divisors of 12 and 18.

Problem 2   In both (1) and (2) below, indicate the set of all the common elements of sets A and B:

(1)   Let A be the set of all divisors of 14; let B be the set of all divisors of 21.

(2)   Let A be the set of all divisors of 16; let B be the set of all divisors of 24.

Among the common divisors of any group of integers, the largest is called the **greatest common divisor**.

Example 1   Let's find the largest common divisor of 12 and 18. Since the divisors of 12 are:

1, 2, 3, 4, 6, 12

and the divisors of 18 are:

1, 2, 3, 6, 9, 18

the common divisors of 12 and 18 are
1, 2, 3, 6,

and the greatest common divisor is 6.

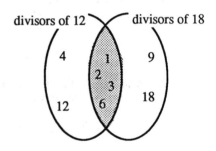

Problem 3   Find all of the common divisors for each of the following groups of numbers, and state for each the greatest common divisor:

(1)   12, 16   (2)   27, 36   (3)   12, 18, 24

When we look at the diagram in Example 1, the divisors of 12 and 18 are divisors of the greatest common divisor 6. In the same way, the common divisors of any integers are the divisors of their greatest common divisor. Once you have found the greatest common divisor, the common divisors can be found by seeking the divisors of the greatest common divisor.

Example 2   Let's find the greatest common divisors of 24, 60, and 84.

(1) Factor each
    number into
    its prime factors.

$$
\begin{array}{rcl}
24 &=& 2 \times 2 \times 2 \times 3 \\
60 &=& 2 \times 2 \times 3 \times 5 \\
84 &=& 2 \times 2 \times 3 \times 7
\end{array}
$$

(2) Multiply together
    each of the
    common factors.

greatest
common $\cdots$ $2 \times 2 \times 3 = 12$
divisor

Note: When there are no common prime factors, the greatest common divisor is 1.

Problem 4   Find the greatest common divisor in each of the following groups of numbers.

(1) $30 = 2 \times 3 \times 5,\ 42 = 2 \times 3 \times 7$ (2)   12, 36

(3)   15, 32   (4)   28, 32, 60

A calculation to find the greatest common divisor of 24, 60, and 84 can also be done in the following manner:

(1) Divide each of the numbers by
    the common prime factors.

          $2\ )\ \ 24\quad 60\quad 84$

(2) Repeat this until there are no
    longer any common prime
    factors.

          $2\ )\ \ 12\quad 30\quad 42$

          $3\ )\ \ \ \ 6\quad 15\quad 21$

(3) Multiply all of the divisors.

                     $2\quad\ \ 5\quad\ \ 7$

greatest
common $\cdots$ $2 \times 2 \times 3 = 12$
divisor

Problem 5   Find the answers to Problem 4 using this method.

Problem 6   Find all common divisors of 24, 60, and 84.

Example 3   A rectangular floor is 90 cm long and 126 cm wide. We would like to cover this entire surface with square tiles of the same size. If we want the tiles to be as large as possible, how many cm long should the sides of the tiles be?

[Approach]   When a rectangle is divided into squares of the same size, the length of one side of a square is a common divisor of the length of the rectangle and its width. To make the side of the square as long as possible, find the greatest common divisor of the length and the width of the rectangle.

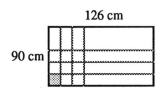

[Solution] $90 = 2 \times 3 \times 3 \times 5$

$126 = 2 \times 3 \times 3 \times 7$

Therefore, since the greatest common divisor of 90 and 126 is

$2 \times 3 \times 3 = 18$

Answer: 18 cm

Problem 7   We want to divide 24 note pads and 36 pencils equally among a given number of children, so that no pads or pencils are left over. If we decide to divide the note pads and pencils among the greatest possible number of children, how many children would that be?

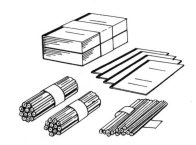

② Common Multiples and Least Common Multiples

Multiples that are shared among integers are the common multiples of those numbers. This you learned in elementary school.

There are an infinite number of common multiples. The smallest of these, other than zero, is called the **least common multiple**.

Example 1   Try to find the least common multiple of 4 and 6:

The multiples of 4 are: 0, 4, 8, 12, 16, 20, 24, 28, 32, 36, ...

The multiples of 6 are: 0, 6, 12, 18, 24, 30, 36, 42, ...

Hence, we can see that the common multiples of 4 and 6 are

0, 12, 24, 36, ...

And the least common multiple is 12.

multiples of 4

multiples of 6

4, 8, 16 20, 28, 32, •••   0, 12, 24, 36, •••   6, 18 30, 42, •••

Looking at the diagram in Example 1, we see that the common multiples of 4 and 6 are multiples of the least common multiple 12. Once we have recognized the least common multiple, we can also find the other common multiples. They are multiples of that number.

Example 2   Let's find the least common multiple of 8, 56, and 140:

(1)   Factor each number into its prime factors.

(2)   Multiply those prime factors common to at least two of the numbers,

2, 2, 2, 7,

by the remaining prime factor, 5.

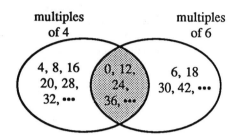

$$8 = 2 \times 2 \times 2$$
$$56 = 2 \times 2 \times 2 \times 7$$
$$140 = 2 \times 2 \times 7 \times 5$$

least common multiple $\cdots 2 \times 2 \times 2 \times 7 = 5$

multiple = 280

Problem 1   Find the least common multiple for each group of numbers:

(1)   12 = 2 x 2 x 3, 30 = 2 x 3 x 5   (2)   12, 18

(3)   15, 21, 35   (4)   16, 28, 48

Another way to calculate the least common multiple of 8, 56, and 140 is as follows:

(1) If there are prime factors shared by at least two of the numbers, use those prime factors to divide the numbers. As for numbers that cannot be divided without remainders, write them below as they are.

$$
\begin{array}{r|rrr}
2 & 8 & 56 & 140 \\ \hline
2 & 4 & 28 & 70 \\ \hline
2 & 2 & 14 & 35 \\ \hline
7 & 1 & 7 & 35 \\ \hline
  & 1 & 7 & 5
\end{array}
$$

least common ... $2 \times 2 \times 2 \times 7 \times 5 = 280$
multiple

(2) Multiply the numbers that remain and all the divisors.

Problem 2 Find the answers to Problem 1 using this method.

Example 3 If we form a square by arranging rectangular cards 12 cm long and 9 cm wide in the same direction, what would be the length of a side of the smallest square we could make?

[Approach] The length of one side of a square formed by placing rectangles in the same direction is the common multiple of the rectangle's length and width. To find the smallest possible length for the side of the square, look for the least common multiple of 12 and 9.

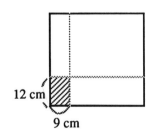

12 cm

9 cm

Problem 3 Find the least common multiple of 12 and 9, and solve Example 3.

Problem 4 From a certain station trains leave every 8 minutes and buses leave every 12 minutes. At 9 o'clock in the morning both a train and a bus left the station. Find the next time on the schedule when a train and a bus will depart together.

Exercises

1. Find the greatest common divisor and least common multiple for each of the following groups of numbers.

    (1) $2 \times 3 \times 5, 2 \times 7$ (2) $2^2 \times 3 \times 5, 2 \times 3^2 \times 5 \times 7$

    (3)   21, 75   (4)   65, 91

    (5)   24, 42, 105

2. Reduce the fraction $\frac{102}{153}$ to its lowest terms. Change $\frac{7}{15}$ and $\frac{1}{12}$ to their least common denominator.

3. A piece of cloth is 56 cm long and 84 cm wide. We would like to cut square handkerchiefs of the same size without leaving any unused cloth. If we make the largest handkerchiefs we can, what would be the length in centimeters of the side of each handkerchief?

4. There are two comets, A and B. A comes close enough to the earth to be observed every 76 years, and B comes close enough every 8 years. If we can observe both of the comets from the earth this year, how many years will it be before we can see them both again?

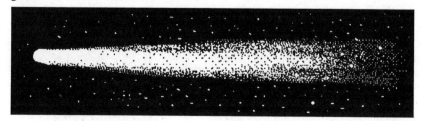

Chapter Exercises

A

1. Factor the following numbers into their prime factors. Then find all of their divisors.

   (1)   24   (2)   30

2. Find the greatest common divisor for each of the following groups of numbers.

   (1)   2 x 2 x 3 x 3, 2 x 3 x 3 x 5   (2)   52, 78   (3)   32, 48, 104

3. Find the least common multiple for each of the following groups of numbers:

   (1)   2 x 3 x 7, 2 x 5 x 7   (2)   42, 63   (3)   12, 15, 20

4. Solve the following problems:

   (1)   If you divide a certain integer x by 7, the quotient is 9 and the remainder is 5. What number is x?

   (2)   Among the integers between 1 and 50, how many multiples of 3 are there?

   (3)   When you divide 40 by certain integers, the remainder is 4. Find all such integers.

5. Three kinds of books are 9 mm, 12 mm, and 15 mm wide, respectively. Placing only books of the same width into 3 stacks of equal height, we want to make the height as small as possible. How many volumes would there be in each stack?

6. A certain factory decided to package its products in cubic boxes, which were to be transported in large containers. The inside of a container is 360 cm long, 240 cm wide, and 200 cm high. If the factory wants to make the boxes as large as possible and also not have any extra space left in the container, how large should a box be (in centimeters)?

B

1. Solve the following problems:

   (1) The greatest common divisor of a certain integer and 6 is 3. List three such integers, starting with the smallest.

   (2) When certain integers are divided by 7, 5 is the remainder. Among these integers, find the one closest to 200.

   (3) When we divide 52 by certain integers, we get 4 as the remainder, and when we divide 78 by those same integers, we get 6 as the remainder. Among these integers, find the largest.

2. A triangular piece of land has 3 sides of 72 m, 96 m, and 108 m. We wish to erect a fence around the land, putting fence posts at equal intervals. If we want to have posts at the three corners and also use as few posts as possible, how many meters should separate the posts? How many posts are necessary?

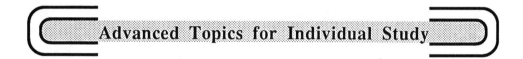

A Method for Finding Multiples

The sum of 39–a multiple of 3–and 12–a multiple of 3–is also a multiple of 3.

$$39 + 12 = 3 \times 13 + 3 \times 4 = 3 \times (13 + 4) = 3 \times 17$$

This is not limited to multiples of 3; it can be said generally that

the sum of any multiples of integer a is a multiple of a.

Applying this principle, you can find multiples of 2, 5, 9, and 3, etc. For example, as in $328 = 320 + 8$, we can express any integer in the following way:

$$\begin{pmatrix} \text{that part including and} \\ \text{above the tens place} \end{pmatrix} + \begin{pmatrix} \text{that part in the} \\ \text{ones place} \end{pmatrix}$$

Since (that part including and above the tens place) is a multiple of 10, it is also a multiple of 2 and a multiple of 5. Accordingly, a number whose ones place is a multiple of 2 is a multiple of 2, and a number whose ones place is a multiple of 5 is a multiple of 5.

To find multiples of 9, think along the lines of the following example:

$$648 = 100 \times 6 + 10 \times 4 + 8 = (99 + 1) \times 6 + (9 + 1) \times 4 + 8$$

$$= (99 \times 6 + 9 \times 4) + (6 + 4 + 8)$$

$$648 = (\text{multiple of } 9) + (6 + 4 + 8)$$

Since 6 + 4 + 8 is a multiple of 9, 648 is a multiple of 9. Generally, a number is a multiple of 9 if the sum of its digits is a multiple of 9.

Since a multiple of 9 is also a multiple of 3, in the same fashion a number is a multiple of 3 if the sum of its digits is a multiple of 3.

Problem 1   Extract the multiples of 2, 3, 5, and 9 from the following numbers:

36, 92, 123, 220, 621

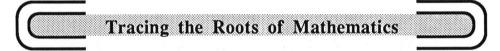

Concerning Prime Numbers

About how many prime numbers are there, anyway?

This is a question that people in ancient Greece thought about, too. In his famous "Elements," which shows us the mathematics of those days, Euclid states that there are any number of prime numbers. To the Greeks there is no doubt that this fact was incomprehensible. They understood that there is an infinity of natural numbers, but the fact that among the natural numbers there is an infinity of prime numbers–numbers used for creating natural numbers by multiplication–was probably truly wondrous for them.

Well, in what ratio do prime numbers appear? For example, from 1 to 10 there are 4 prime numbers: 2, 3, 5, and 7. By 100 there are 25 prime numbers, but this is less than ten times the number of primes (4) from 1 to 10. By 1,000 there are 168 prime numbers, but this is less than ten times the number of primes (25) from 1 to 100. And by 10,000 there are 1,229 prime numbers, but, as you can guess, this is less than ten times the number of primes (168) from 1 to 1,000. In this way, the rate at which prime numbers occur decreases little by little.

There is also an interesting conjecture with regard to prime numbers:

"Even numbers larger than 4 are the sum of two prime numbers."

For example,

4 = 2 + 2, 6 = 3 + 3, 8 = 3 + 5, 10 = 3 + 7, etc.

However, we still don't know whether or not this is true.

CHAPTER 2

POSITIVE AND NEGATIVE NUMBERS

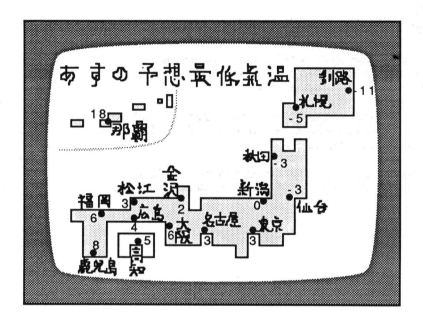

Do you know the difference between using black ink and using red ink? When dealing with money the two distinguish between surplus and deficit. For example, if you have a surplus of 300 yen, the amount is usually written in black ink. On the other hand, if you have a deficit of 300 yen, the amount is usually written in red ink. In cases where it is impossible to change the color of the ink, the 300 written in black ink can be changed to +300, and instead of writing 300 in red ink, it can be written as -300. Numbers with these signs can also be used in such areas as weather forecasting to indicate air temperature.

POSITIVE AND NEGATIVE NUMBERS

   Numbers with Signs

Temperatures lower than 0° C are expressed using the symbol -, which is read **minus**. For example, the temperature that is 3° below 0° C is written -3° C.

On the other hand, temperatures higher than 0° C, such as 5° C, may be written with the symbol +, as in +5° C. This is read **plus** five degrees Centigrade (or Celsius).

When the symbols + and - are used in this way, the + is called a **plus sign** and - is called a **minus sign**.

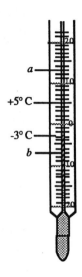

Problem 1   With numbers marked by either + or -, express the position of *a* and *b* in the diagram above.

Problem 2   With numbers marked by either + or -, express the following temperatures:

(1)   5° C below 0° C   (2)   22° C above 0° C

(3)   2.6° C below 0° C   (4) $\frac{1}{2}$ ° C above 0° C

Numbers like -5 and -2.6 are called **negative numbers**, while numbers like +5 and +2.6 are called **positive numbers**.

+5 and +2.6 are the same numbers that you have seen as 5 and 2.6 .   0 is neither positive nor negative.

From this point on, "numbers" will be taken to mean positive numbers, 0, and negative numbers. For example, an integer can be a positive number, 0, or a negative number. Fractions and decimals can be negative, as in $-\frac{4}{5}$ and -2.6. Natural numbers are positive integers.

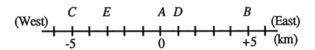

$$\ldots, \; -3, \; -2, \; -1, \; 0, \; 1, \; 2, \; 3, \; \ldots$$

Positive numbers and negative numbers can be used to express some opposing characteristics.

Example 1 If position B is 5 km to the east of central position A and is expressed as +5 km, then position C, which is 5 km to the west of central position A, can be expressed as -5 km.

Problem 3 In the diagram above express positions D, E, and A.

Problem 4 When it is said that the altitude of Mt. Fuji is +3776 m and the altitude of the Dead Sea is -392 m, what do the + and - express?

Example 2 If we indicate moving forward 4 m as moving +4 m, then we could indicate moving backward 5 m as moving -5 m.

Problem 5 If the water level of a dam rises 3 m and we express the change in water level as +3 m, then if the water level comes down 3 m, how would we express the change in water level?

Problem 6 If we express a profit of 500 yen as +500 yen, what does -300 yen express?

Comparison of Numbers

The Number Line

In the following manner, positive and negative numbers can be made to correspond to the points on a number line.

First, choose one point which will serve as the standard of the number line, and let that point correspond to 0. This point is called the **origin**. Left or right from the origin one can create a series of marks at defined intervals. Moving to the right, each mark will correspond to the positive numbers

$$+1, +2, +3, ...$$

and moving to the left, each mark will correspond to the negative numbers

$$-1, -2, -3, ...$$

If the defined space is taken as the unit of space, fractions and decimals, both positive and negative, correspond to points on a line. For example,

a point at a distance of 1.2 to the right is +1.2

a point at a distance of $\frac{8}{5}$ to the left is $-\frac{8}{5}$

This line is a number line.

In this instance, we say that the direction to the right is the **positive direction** and the direction to the left is the **negative direction**.

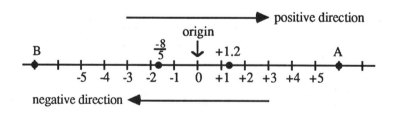

Problem 1   On the above number line, give the numbers that correspond to points *A* and *B*.

Problem 2 Construct a number line and then mark off the points that correspond to the following numbers:

(1) +1.5   (2) $-\dfrac{1}{2}$ (3) $+\dfrac{5}{2}$

(4) -2.5   (5) $-4\dfrac{1}{2}$

Comparison of Numbers

For a positive number, if the number becomes larger, the point that corresponds to it on the number line moves in the positive direction. Even if you include 0 and negative numbers, the farther a number moves in the positive direction on a number line, the larger the number that corresponds to that point. On the other hand, the farther you move in the negative direction, the smaller the number corresponding to that point becomes.

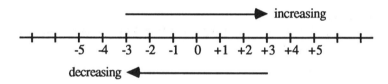

Example 1 Since the point for +4.5 is to the right of the point for +2.3,

$$+2.3 < +4.5,$$

and since the point for -4 is to the left of the point for -1,

$$-4 < -1.$$

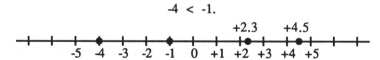

Problem 3 Use inequality symbols to show the inequality of the following pairs of numbers:

(1) +4, -5   (2) -3.5, 0   (3) $-\dfrac{4}{5}$, -1

When we think of three or more numbers, for example, -3, 0, and +5, -3 is smaller than 0 and 0 is smaller than +5. That is to say,

$$-3 < 0 \text{ and } 0 < +5.$$

We can express these together as

$$-3 < 0 < +5$$

or as

$$+5 > 0 > -3.$$

Signs and Comparison

Positive numbers are greater than 0, and negative numbers are less than 0.

(negative number) < 0 < (positive number)

(**Problem 4**)   Use inequality symbols to express the relations among the following series of numbers:

(1)   5, 0, 0.5   (2)   -0.1, -0.01, -1   (3)   +6, -9, -4

Absolute Value

On a number line, we see that the distance between the origin and a point which expresses the value of a number is the **absolute value**. For example, since +3 is at a distance of 3 from the origin, the absolute value of +3 is 3. Likewise, since -3 is at a distance of 3 from the origin, the absolute value of -3 is 3. The absolute value of 0 is 0.

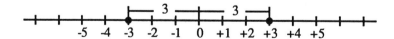

We can see that the absolute value of a number is equal to the number remaining after the positive or negative sign has been removed.

Problem 5   Find the absolute values of the following numbers:

(1)   +8   (2)   -10   (3)   2.5

(4) $-\dfrac{1}{3}$ (5) $\dfrac{5}{6}$

Problem 6   Give the numbers whose absolute value is 7.

Using the concept of absolute value, you can identify the size of a positive number or a negative number in the following manner.

> **Absolute Values and Comparison**
>
> With a positive number, the larger the absolute value the larger the number.
>
> With a negative number, the larger the absolute value the smaller the number.

Problem 7   List the integers, from largest to smallest, whose absolute value is less than 5.

Exercises

1.   Rewrite the following phrases using positive numbers:

(1)   -500 yen profit   (2)   -10 min from now.

(3)   -2 kg increase in weight   (4)   -4° C decrease in temperature

2.   Express each of the following as positive or negative numbers, and mark their positions on a number line:

(1)   The number which is 5 greater than 0.

(2)   The number which is 6 less than 0.

(3)   The number which is 3.5 less than 0.

(4)   The number which is $1\frac{2}{5}$ greater than 0.

3.   In each of the following groups of numbers, use inequality signs to express the differences in size:

(1)   0.2, -2   (2)   0, -0.8, -1.5   (3) $-\frac{1}{2}, \frac{1}{3}, -\frac{1}{5}$

4.   Arrange the following numbers in order from smallest to largest:

$-\frac{2}{3}$, -2, 0.2, -0.2, 1, -1, 0

ADDITION AND SUBTRACTION

 Addition

The operation of adding is called **addition**. The result of addition is called a sum.

Addition of Positive and Negative Numbers

We have a tank for storing water. If we put in or take out water, the water level in the tank goes up or down. If we express a change which raises the water level with a positive number, then we can express a change which lowers the water level with a negative number.

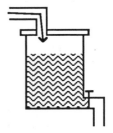

Example 1 If the water level rises 5 cm,

the change in the water level is +5 cm.

If the water level decreases 3 cm,

the change in the water level is -3 cm.

Problem 1 What is meant by "the change in the water level is +2 cm"?
What is meant by "the change in the water level is -4 cm"?

When the water level changes twice in succession, we can express the changes, starting with the first change, as:

(the first change) + (the second change).

(1) If the first change is: +3 cm
     and the second change is: +5 cm,
     then the total change is: +8 cm. That is,

$$(+3) + (+5) = +8 \tag{1}$$

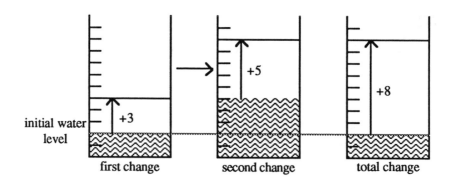

initial water level

first change   second change   total change

(2)   If the first change is: -3 cm
      and the second change is: -5 cm,
      then the total change is:

$$(-3) + (-5)$$

and this is -8 cm.

$$(-3) + (-5) = -8$$ (2)

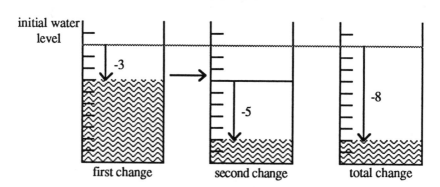

initial water level

first change   second change   total change

(3)   If the first change is: +3 cm
      and the second change is: -8 cm,
      then the total change is:

$$(+3) + (-8)$$

and this is -5 cm.

$$(+3) + (-8) = -5$$ (3)

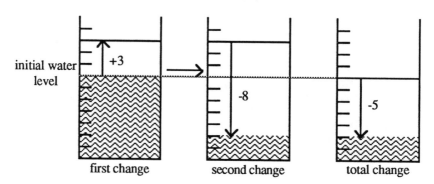

initial water level

first change   second change   total change

(4) If the first change is: -3 cm
     and the second change is: +8 cm,
     then the total change is:

$$(-3) + (+8)$$

and this is +5 cm.

$$(-3) + (+8) = +5 \qquad\qquad (4)$$

first change   second change   total change

initial water
level

(**Problem 2**) Write the following changes as expressions, and find the total change
in cm for each one.

(1) first change... +4 cm,   second change... +3 cm

(2) first change... -5 cm,   second change... -1 cm

(3) first change... +5 cm,   second change... -2 cm

(4) first change... -6 cm,   second change... +6 cm

(**Problem 3**) In the expressions for (1)–(4) above, which are examples of adding
numbers with the same sign? And which are examples of adding
numbers with different signs? In each case, what is the absolute value
of the sum, and how did the signs change?

The Sum of Numbers with the Same Sign

In seeking the sum of two numbers with the same
sign, you can assign the common sign to the sum of the
absolute values.

Example 2   (1) $(+5) + (+6) = +(5 + 6) = +11$

(2) $(-5) + (-6) = -(5 + 6) = -11$

Problem 4   Calculate the following:

(1) $(+3) + (+7)$ (2) $(-11) + (-8)$

(3) $(+3.2) + (+1.5)$ (4) $(-\frac{1}{5}) + (-\frac{3}{5})$

The Sum of Numbers with Different Signs

In seeking the sum of two numbers with different signs, consider only their absolute values and subtract the smaller absolute value from the larger. Then assign to the sum the sign of the number with the larger absolute value. If the absolute values are equal, then the sum is 0.

Example 3   (1) $(+8) + (-7) = +(8 - 7)$
$$= +1$$

(2) $(+6) + (-10) = -(10 - 6)$
$$= -4$$

(3) $(-3) + (+3) = 0$

Problem 5   Calculate the following:

(1) $(+6) + (-2)$ (2) $(+3) + (-5)$

(3) $(-4) + (+7)$ (4) $(-7) + (+7)$

(5) $(+1.5) + (-2)$ (6) $(+\frac{1}{2}) + (-\frac{1}{3})$

No matter what number you add to 0, the sum is the same as that number. And, if you add 0 to any number, the sum will always be that number. That is,

$$a + 0 = a$$

$$0 + a = a$$

The Commutative Law and the Associative Law of Addition

As you learned in elementary school, when adding two positive numbers, even if you reverse the order of the numbers the sum does not change. This is valid for both positive and negative numbers. This law of calculation is called the **commutative law of addition**.

$$(+5) + (-3) = (-3) + (+5)$$

$$a + b = b + a$$

Problem 6   Do the following calculations and compare the sums:

$$\{(+3) + (-9)\} + (+7), \ (+3) + \{(-9) + (+7)\}$$

As for the addition of positive and negative numbers, the following computation law holds; it is called the **associative law of addition**.

$$(a + b) + c = a + (b + c)$$

Because of the commutative and associative laws of addition, when we add positive and negative numbers it does not matter how they are combined or in what order they are given. Therefore, when we are adding many numbers it is advisable to calculate the sum of all positive numbers and the sum of all negative numbers.

Example 4

$$
\begin{aligned}
(+3) + (-8) + (+7) + (-5) &= (+3) + (+7) + (-8) + (-5) \\
&= \{(+3) + (+7)\} + \{(-8) + (-5)\} \\
&= (+10) + (-13) \\
&= -3
\end{aligned}
$$

Problem 7   Calculate the following:

(1) $(-4) + (+5) + (-3) + (-1) + (+8)$

(2) $(+5) + 0 + (-3) + (+6)$

(3) $(-4) + (+1) + (-5) + (-7)$

Drills

1. Calculate the following:

(1)   (+5) + (+9)   (2)   (-6) + (+8)   (3)   (-4) + (-7)

(4)   0 + (-3)   (5)   (-3.5) + (-1.5)   (6)   (-0.4) + (+0.2)

(7) $(+\frac{3}{5}) + (-\frac{1}{5})$ (8) $(-\frac{2}{3}) + (-\frac{1}{9})$ (9) $(-\frac{1}{2}) + (-\frac{3}{7})$

(10) $(-\frac{3}{5}) + (+\frac{1}{2}) + (-0.9)$

 Subtraction

The operation of subtracting is called **subtraction**, and the result of subtraction is the difference.

When a water level changes twice consecutively, you can find the total change by using the following calculation.

(first change) + (second change) = (total change)

This time you don't know the first change, but you do know the second change and the total change. In such cases, use the following calculation to find the first change.

(total change) – (second change)

(1)   If the second change is: +2 cm
      and the total change is: +6 cm,
      you can calculate the first change as: (+6) – (+2).
      The difference is represented in the following diagram as x.

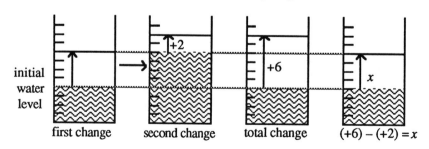

initial
water
level

first change   second change   total change   (+6) – (+2) = x

Problem 1 Find the difference using the diagram.

You can think of (1) in the following way.

(1') Since the second change was +2 cm and the total change was +6 cm, to go back to the first change it is useful to make the second change -2 cm. Then, if you calculate

$$(+6) + (-2)$$

you can find the first change.

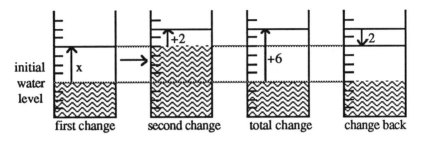

first change   second change   total change   change back

When we compare (1) and (1'), we arrive at the following expression.

$$(+6) - (+2) = (+6) + (-2) = +4$$

Subtracting +2 is the same as adding -2.

(2) If the second change is: -3 cm
and the total change is: +1 cm,
you can calculate the first change as: $(+1) - (-3)$.

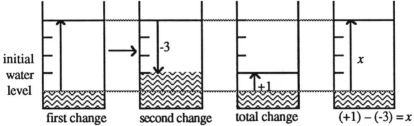

first change   second change   total change $(+1) - (-3) = x$

You can also think of (2) in the following way.

(2') Since the second change was -3 cm and the total change was +1 cm, to go back to the first change it is useful to make the second change +3 cm. Then, if you calculate

$$(+1) + (+3)$$

you can find the first change.

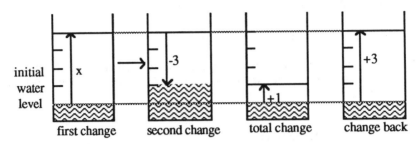

initial
water
level

first change   second change   total change   change back

When we compare (2) and (2'), we arrive at the following expression.

$$(+1) - (-3) = (+1) + (+3) = +4$$

Subtracting -3 is the same as adding +3.

(**Problem 2**) Change the following expressions so that they involve addition.

(1)   (+7) – (+5)   (2)   (-6) – (-4)

**The Difference of Positive and
Negative Numbers**

Subtracting a positive number or a negative number
is the same as changing the sign of that number and
adding it.

(**Example 1**) (1)   (+3) – (+5) = (+3) + (-5)   = -2

(2)   (-3) – (-7) = (-3) + (+7)   = +4

(**Example 2**) (1)   0 – (+6) = 0 + (-6)   = -6

(2)   0 – (-6) = 0 + (+6)   = +6

As seen in Example 2, subtracting a number from 0 is the same as changing the
number's sign.

Further, in subtracting 0 from any number, the difference is always the original
number.

$$a - 0 = a$$

Problem 3 Calculate the following:

(1) $(+7) - (+3)$ (2) $(+8) - (-4)$ (3) $(-5) - (+7)$

(4) $(-6) - (-1)$ (5) $(+7) - (+9)$ (6) $(-5) - (-5)$

(7) $(+4.2) - 0$ (8) $0 - (-\frac{1}{5})$ (9) $(-\frac{6}{7}) - (-\frac{1}{7})$

Example 3 $6 - 9 = (+6) - (+9) = (+6) + (-9) = -3$

In elementary school, where you were taught only about positive numbers and 0, you thought that you could not subtract a larger number from a smaller number. However, if you also consider negative numbers, you can subtract any number from any other number.

Problem 4 If you subtract a positive number from some number, can the result be larger than the original number? Can it be smaller than the original number? What about subtracting a negative number?

Drills

1. Perform the following calculations:

(1) $(-3) - (+2)$ (2) $(-4) - (-7)$ (3) $0 - (-5)$

(4) $(+1.2) - (-0.2)$ (5) $(-\frac{2}{5}) - (+\frac{3}{10})$

3 **Calculations That Combine Addition and Subtraction**

Since subtraction can be changed to addition, you can change an expression that combines addition and subtraction to an expression involving only addition.

Example 1 $(+9) + (-4) - (+8) - (-6) = (+9) + (-4) + (-8) + (+6)$

Problem 1   Convert the following expressions so that they involve only addition.

(1) $(+8) - (-2) - (+5)$ (2) $(-3) - (+6) + (-7) - (-2)$

Earlier you learned how to do addition-only problems, as on the left below. You can also do these problems without using the addition symbols or parentheses, as on the right below.

$$
\begin{array}{ll}
& (+9) \; + \; (-4) \; + \; (-8) \; + \; (+6) \\
= & (+9) \; + \; (+6) \; + \; (-4) \; + \; (-8) \\
= & (+15) \; + \; (-12) \\
= & +3
\end{array}
\qquad
\begin{array}{ll}
& 9 \; - \; 4 \; - \; 8 \; + \; 6 \\
= & 9 \; + \; 6 \; - \; 4 \; - \; 8 \\
= & 15 \; - \; 12 \\
= & 3
\end{array}
$$

$$(+9) \; + \; (-4) \; + \; (-8) \; + \; (+6)$$

$$\updownarrow \qquad \updownarrow \qquad \updownarrow \qquad \updownarrow$$

$$9 \qquad -4 \qquad -8 \qquad +6$$

Note: If the first number of an expression or an answer is a positive number, it is customary not to write the + sign.

Example 2 $
\begin{aligned}
(+2) - (+7) - (-9) + (-5) \; &= (+2) + (-7) + (+9) + (-5) \\
&= 2 - 7 + 9 - 5 \\
&= 2 + 9 - 7 - 5 \\
&= 11 - 12 \\
&= -1
\end{aligned}
$

Problem 2   Do the calculation for Problem 1 by following the steps of Example 2.

Example 3 $
\begin{aligned}
-17 - (-35) + 3 + (-14) \; &= -17 + 35 + 3 - 14 \\
&= 35 + 3 - 17 - 14 \\
&= 38 - 31 \\
&= 7
\end{aligned}
$

Problem 3   Calculate the following:

(1) $9 + (-3) - (-5)$ (2) $10 - (+28) + 55$

(3) $-37 - (-71) + 0 - 6$ (4) $-5.3 + (-6.1) - (-3.4)$

(5) $3 - 7 - 2 + 4$ (6) $-5 + 4 - 1 + 7 - 6$

Exercises

1. Calculate the following:

   (1) $(-4) + (+5)$

   (2) $(+7) - (-6)$

   (3) $(-9) - (-2)$

   (4) $(-18) + (-14)$

   (5) $(+2.3) - (+8)$

   (6) $(-\frac{3}{5}) - (-\frac{4}{5})$

2. Calculate the following:

   (1) $3 - (+6) + (-8)$

   (2) $-4 + (-1) + 7$

   (3) $1 - 3 + 5 - 4$

   (4) $-6 - (-19) + (-11)$

   (5) $-4 + 14 + 10 - 21 - 9$

   (6) $2 - (+7.8) - (-5) - 2.2$

   (7) $\frac{1}{4} - (+\frac{2}{3}) - (-\frac{3}{4}) + (-\frac{1}{3})$

3. Answer the following questions about the chart.

   (1) How much higher was the temperature at 8 o'clock than at 6 o'clock?

   (2) How much higher was the temperature at 10 o'clock than at 6 o'clock?

Time	Temp. (°C)
6:00	-7.5
8:00	-6.4
10:00	3.2

MULTIPLICATION AND DIVISION

   ## Multiplication

The operation of multiplying is called **multiplication**, and the result of multiplication is a product.

Multiplication of Positive and Negative Numbers

When we let water into a tank, the water level rose 10 cm each minute. When we stopped letting water in and started letting it out, it went down 6 cm each minute.

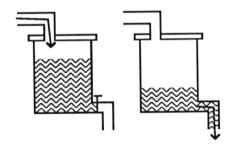

As in the case of addition, when we assigned positive numbers to the raising of the water level and negative numbers to the lowering of the water level, the change for each minute can be expressed in the following way.

Letting water in: +10 (cm)

Letting water out: -6 (cm)

Furthermore, a change in the water level can be expressed:

(change for each minute) × (time)

First, we will look at the case of letting water in.

(1)   For example, in 3 minutes the level of the water will rise 30 cm. We can express this as

$$(+10) \times (+3) \quad = +30 \tag{1}$$

(2)   The level of the water 3 minutes before was 30 cm lower than it is now. Since 3 minutes before means -3 minutes after, we can express this as

$$(+10) \times (-3) \quad = -30 \tag{2}$$

The Case of Letting Water In

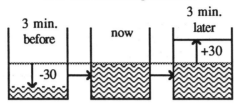

Problem 1   In this case of letting water in, find the level of the water in 4 minutes; 4 minutes ago; 1 minute ago; in 0 minutes.

We will now look at the case of letting water out.

(3)   In 3 minutes the level of the water will be 18 cm lower than it is now. We can express this as

$$(-6) \times (+3) = -18 \qquad\qquad (3)$$

(4)   3 minutes ago the surface of the water was 18 cm higher than it is now. We can express this as

$$(-6) \times (-3) = +18 \qquad\qquad (4)$$

The Case of Letting Water Out

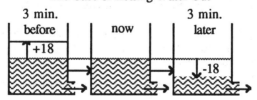

Problem 2   In this case of letting water out, find the level of the water compared to the present level in 5 minutes; 6 minutes ago; in 1 minute.

Problem 3   In which of the expressions (1)–(4) are we multiplying numbers with the same sign? In which are we multiplying numbers with different signs? In each case explain how the absolute value of the product and the sign will change.

The Product of Numbers with the Same Sign

When seeking the product of two numbers with the same sign, you can assign a plus sign to the product of the absolute values.

Example 1   (1)   (+3) x (+4) = +(3 x 4)   (+) x (+) → (+)

= +12

(2)   (-3) x (-4)   = +(3 x 4)
                                                                 (-) x (-)   → (+)
= +12

Problem 4   Calculate the following:

(1)   (+3) x (+2)   (2)   (-4) x (-5)

(3)   (+7) x (+1.5)   (4)   (-11) x (-6)

The Product of Numbers with Different Signs

When seeking the product of two numbers with different signs, you can assign a minus sign to the product of the absolute values.

Example 2   (1)   (-8) x (+3) = -(8 x 3)   (-) x (+) → (-)

= -24

(2)   (+8) x (-3)   = -(8 x 3)
                                                                 (+) x (-)   → (-)
= -24

Problem 5 Calculate the following:

(1) (-7) × (+4)

(2) (+5) × (-4)

(3) (-9) × (+10)

(4) (+13) × (-5)

(5) (-16) × (+3)

(6) (+2.5) × (-0.6)

(7) (-1.4) × (+1.5)

(8) $(+\frac{3}{4}) \times (-\frac{1}{3})$

Problem 6 Give the product of -1 and each of the following numbers, and compare these products to the original numbers:

$$+3, \quad -3, \quad +5, \quad -5$$

Finding the product of -1 and a number is equivalent to changing the sign of that number.

Example 3 (-1) × 6 = (-1) × (+6)

= -6

Thus, -6 is the same as (-1) × 6. Further, -(-3) is the same as (-1) × (-3).

Example 4 (1) -(-3) = (-1) × (-3)

= +3

(2) -(-1) = +1

Problem 7 Simplify the following numbers:

(1) -(-5)

(2) $-(-\frac{1}{2})$

(3) -(+2)

(4) $-(+\frac{2}{3})$

If you multiply any number by 1, the product is the same number. And if you multiply 1 by any number, the product is the same as the number you multiplied by.

$$a \times 1 = a, \quad 1 \times a = a$$

If you multiply any number by 0 or if you multiply 0 by any number, the product is 0.

$$a \times 0 = 0, \quad 0 \times a = 0$$

The Commutative Law and the Associative Law of Multiplication

As you learned in elementary school, with two positive numbers, regardless of the order of the multiplier and the multiplicand, the product does not change. This also holds for positive and negative numbers. This law of calculation is called the **commutative law of multiplication**.

$$(+2) \times (-3) = (-3) \times (+2)$$

$$a \times b = b \times a$$

(**Problem 8**)   Perform the following calculations and compare the products:

$$\{(+2) \times (-3)\} \times (-4), \ (+2) \times \{(-3) \times (-4)\}$$

With positive and negative numbers, the following calculation law, called the **associative law of multiplication**, holds.

$$(a \times b) \times c = a \times (b \times c)$$

Because of the commutative and associative laws of multiplication, when you multiply any positive and negative numbers, you can combine and rearrange the numbers in any order you want.

(**Example 5**)   (1) $(-1.5) \times (+1.5) \times (-2) = (-2.25) \times (-2)$

$$= +4.5$$

(2) $(-1.5) \times (-2) \times (+1.5) = (+3) \times (+1.5)$

$$= +4.5$$

Problem 9   Try to calculate each of the following expressions by changing the order.

(1)   (-2.5) × (-2.7) × (+16)

(2)   (+12.5) × (-3.9) × (-8)

Problem 10   If you multiply a number by a positive number, the sign does not change. If you multiply that number by 1, 2, 3, or 4 negative numbers, how does the sign change?

The Sign of a Product

When you multiply positive numbers and negative numbers, the sign of the product will be minus if there are an odd number of negative numbers, and plus if there are an even number of negative numbers.

The absolute value of the product of any multiplied numbers is the product of the absolute values of those numbers.

Example 6   (1)   (-2) × (-8) × (+2) × (-4) × (-5)   = +(2 × 8 × 2 × 4 × 5)

= 640

(2) $(-\frac{1}{2}) \times (-8) \times (-\frac{7}{4})$ = $-(\frac{1}{2} \times 8 \times \frac{7}{4})$

= -7

Note: When an operation sign and the plus or minus sign of a number appear in succession, use parentheses. For example, when the expression is 3 × (-5), do not write 3 × -5.

Problem 11 Calculate the following:

    (1) $(-6) \times (-3) \times (+5)$ (2) $5 \times (-3) \times 2$

    (3) $(-1.4) \times 0 \times 2.5$ (4) $(-\frac{5}{3}) \times (-2) \times (-\frac{7}{5}) \times \frac{9}{14}$

Example 7   (1) $(-4)^3 = (-4) \times (-4) \times (-4)$

$$= -64$$

    (2) $(-3)^4 = (-3) \times (-3) \times (-3) \times (-3)$

$$= 81$$

    (3) $-3^4 = -(3 \times 3 \times 3 \times 3)$

$$= -81$$

Note: The -3^4 in (3) above is different from the $(-3)^4$ in (2). It is 3^4 with a minus sign attached.

Problem 12 Explain each of the following pairs of numbers by writing out their products, and then compare the results of the calculations.

    (1) $(-4)^2, -4^2$ (2) $(-5)^3, -5^3$

Problem 13 Calculate the following:

    (1) $(-3^2) \times (-10)^3$ (2) $(-4)^2 \times (-2^3)$

Drills

1. Calculate the following:

    (1) $(-5) \times (+3)$ (2) $(-6) \times (-2)$

    (3) $(-1.2) \times (-0.5)$ (4) $(-6) \times \dfrac{2}{3} \times \dfrac{1}{2}$

    (5) $(-1) \times 9$ (6) $-(-7)$

    (7) $(-3) \times 6 \times (-9) \times (-2)$ (8) -2^4

 Division

The operation of dividing is called **division**, and the result of division is a quotient.

Division of Positive and Negative Numbers

A calculation by division is the opposite of a calculation by multiplication.

$$2 \times 3 = 6, \qquad 6 \div 3 = 2$$

Example 1 We do not know how much the water level in a tank changes each minute, but we do know that in 3 minutes the water level will be 6 cm lower. In such cases, since we know that

(change each minute) $\times (+3) = -6,$ (1)

we can calculate the change each minute as

$$(-6) \div (+3).$$

Problem 1   Looking for the value of the (change each minute) to satisfy (1) in Example 1, find the answer for $(-6) \div (+3)$.

Similarly, since $(+2) \times (+3) = +6$
$$(+6) \div (+3) = +2.$$

Since $(-2) \times (+3) = -6$
$$(-6) \div (+3) = -2.$$

Since $(-2) \times (-3) = +6$
$$(+6) \div (-3) = -2.$$

Since $(+2) \times (-3) = -6$
$$(-6) \div (-3) = +2.$$

Signs and Absolute Values of Quotients

(1)   When finding the quotient of numbers with the same signs, you can assign a plus sign to the quotient of the absolute values.

(2)   When finding the quotient of numbers with different signs, you can assign a minus sign to the quotient of the absolute values.

Also, when $a \neq 0$, $0 \div a = 0$.

Note: Writing $a \neq b$ shows that a and b are not equal.

Example 2   (1) $(+12) \div (+4) = +(12 \div 4)$ $(+) \div (+) \rightarrow (+)$
$$= +3$$

(2) $(-12) \div (-4) = +(12 \div 4)$ $(-) \div (-) \rightarrow (+)$
$$= +3$$

(3) $(+12) \div (-4) = -(12 \div 4)$ $(+) \div (-) \rightarrow (-)$
$$= -3$$

(4) $(-12) \div (+4) = -(12 \div 4)$ $(-) \div (+) \rightarrow (-)$
$$= -3$$

Problem 2   Calculate the following:

(1)   (-26) ÷ (+2)   (2)   (-32) ÷ (-8)

(3)   0 ÷ (-7)   (4)   18 ÷ (-6)

(5)   (-54) ÷ 9   (6)   0.5 ÷ (-0.2)

Example 3 $\frac{-3}{5} = (-3) \div 5 = -(3 \div 5) = -\frac{3}{5}$

Accordingly, $\frac{-3}{5} = -\frac{3}{5}$

Problem 3   Check that $\frac{3}{-5} = -\frac{3}{5}$ as in Example 3.

Reciprocals

When the product of two numbers is 1, each number is said to be the reciprocal of the other number.

Example 4   (1)   Since $3 \times \frac{1}{3} = 1$, the reciprocal of 3 is $\frac{1}{3}$, and the reciprocal of $\frac{1}{3}$ is 3.

(2)   Since $(-\frac{3}{4}) \times (-\frac{4}{3}) = 1$, the reciprocal of $-\frac{3}{4}$ is $-\frac{4}{3}$.

In this way, the reciprocal of a positive or negative number is the reciprocal of the absolute value with the plus or minus sign of the original number. Furthermore, since the product of 0 and any number cannot equal 1, 0 has no reciprocal.

Problem 4   Find the reciprocals of the following numbers:

(1) $\frac{3}{10}$ (2)   -1   (3) $-\frac{15}{4}$

(4)   1   (5)   -0.5

Problem 5   Compare the results derived from calculating $10 \div (-2)$ and $10 \times (-\frac{1}{2})$.

Division and Reciprocals

Dividing by a positive or negative number is the same as multiplying by the reciprocal of that number.

Example 5 $\frac{8}{9} \div (-\frac{2}{3}) = \frac{8}{9} \times (-\frac{3}{2}) = -\frac{4}{3}$

Problem 6   Calculate the following:

(1) $5 \div (-10)$ (2) $-\frac{2}{7} \div (-4)$

(3) $-3 \div \frac{1}{3}$ (4) $24 \div (-\frac{6}{5})$

(5) $(-\frac{9}{8}) \div (-\frac{3}{4})$ (6) $(-1\frac{1}{2}) \div 6$

Calculations That Include Both Multiplication and Division

An expression which mixes multiplication and division can be converted to an expression involving only multiplication.

Example 6   (1) $15 \div (-7) \times (-2\frac{4}{5}) = 15 \times (-\frac{1}{7}) \times (-\frac{14}{5})$

$$= +6$$

(2) $(-2)^3 \div (-4^2) \div (-6) = (-8) \div (-16) \div (-6)$

$$= (-8) \times (-\frac{1}{16}) \times (-\frac{1}{6})$$

$$= -\frac{1}{12}$$

Problem 7   Convert the following expressions so that they involve only multiplication, and then calculate them.

(1) $(-12) \div 4 \times (-16)$

(2) $(-15) \times (-2) \div (-18)$

(3) $(-1\frac{2}{3}) \times \frac{8}{15} \div (-1\frac{1}{2})$

(4) $(-2^3) \times 3^2 \div (-4^2)$

Drills

1. Calculate the following:

(1) $(-12) \div (+3)$

(2) $35 \div (-7)$

(3) $(-18) \div (-6)$

(4) $0.24 \div (-4)$

(5) $(-1.5) \div 0.3$

(6) $(-4)^3 \div (-2^2)$

(7) $(-8) \div (+2) \times (-3)$

(8) $72 \div (-9) \div (-2)^2$

(9) $(-\frac{28}{15}) \div (+\frac{7}{9})$

(10) $(-5^2) \div 10 \times (-\frac{2}{5})$

 ### Calculations in Which the Four Arithmetic Operations Are Mixed

Addition, subtraction, multiplication, and division taken together are called the **four arithmetic operations**.

Even in calculating expressions which include negative numbers, when the four arithmetic operations are mixed, do the multiplication and the division first, and do the addition and subtraction later.

Example 1   (1) $(-4) \times (-3) - (-5)$ $= 12 - (-5)$

$= 12 + 5$

$= 17$

(2) $(-5) - 6 + (-3)$ $= (-5) - (-2)$

$= -5 + 2$

$= -3$

Problem 1   Calculate the following:

(1) $(-2) \times 3 \, (-5)$ (2) $(-7) - 8 + (-4)$

(3) $(+16) + (-2) - (-7)$ (4) $-27 - 6 \times (-5)$

(5) $(-3) \times (-4) - (-5) \times 2$ (6) $60 + \{(-6) - (+4)\}$

Example 2   (1) $10 - (-3)^2 \times 4$ $= 10 - 9 \times 4$

$= 10 - 36$

$= -26$

(2) $(\frac{3}{4} - 0.25) + (-1.5)$ $= (\frac{3}{4} - \frac{1}{4}) + (-\frac{3}{2})$

$= \frac{1}{2} \times (-\frac{2}{3})$

$= -\frac{1}{3}$

Problem 2   Calculate the following:

(1) $4^2 - 3 \times 6$ (2) $-5 \times 2 + (-3)^2$

(3) $8 - (-4)^2 \times 2$ (4) $\{(-3)^2 - 2^2\} + 5 - (-7)$

(5) $-4 \times 0.4 + (-3.6)$ (6) $-1.5 - (-9) + (-3)$

The Distributive Law

The following law of calculation holds true. It is called the **distributive law**.

$$(a + b) \times c = a \times c + b \times c$$

$$c \times (a + b) = c \times a + c \times b$$

Problem 3   Calculate the following and compare the answers.

(1) $\{(-5) + (-7)\} \times (+3)$, $(-5) \times (+3) + (-7) \times (+3)$

(2) $(-6) \times \{10 + (-7)\}$, $(-6) \times 10 + (-6) \times (-7)$

Exercises

1.   Calculate the following:

(1) $(-7) \times (-6)$

(2) $(+3) \times (-9)$

(3) $(-2.4) \times (+5)$

(4) $(+\frac{3}{4}) \times (+\frac{8}{15})$

(5) $(+38) \div (-19)$

(6) $(-7) \div (+9)$

(7) $-\frac{5}{6} \div (-10)$

(8) $(+\frac{5}{6}) \div (+\frac{1}{3})$

2.   Calculate the following:

(1) $(-3) + (-5) \times (-2)$

(2) $(-3) \times 4 - (-7)$

(3) $8 - (-24) \div (-6)$

(4) $12 \div (-3) + (-6) \times 2$

(5) $(-7) \times 6 - 25 \div (-5)$

(6) $(-1.5) \div 3 + (-0.1)$

(7) $\frac{2}{3} - (-\frac{1}{3}) \times \frac{1}{2}$

(8) $(-\frac{3}{10}) \times (-5) \div 3 - (-\frac{1}{4})$

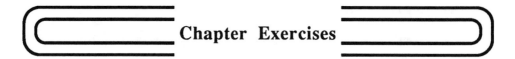

Chapter Exercises

A

1. Using inequality symbols, show the relations of the following groups of numbers:

    (1)   0, 3

    (2) $-\frac{3}{10}, -\frac{1}{3}$

    (3) $\frac{3}{4}, -\frac{5}{3}$

    (4)   0, -4, 2

    (5) $-0.6, -\frac{1}{2}, -\frac{2}{3}$

2. Write all those numbers which have absolute values of 3.5, 12, or 0, arranging them from smallest to largest.

3. Find the appropriate numbers to fill in the following blanks.

    (1)   The number which is 3 less than 0 is _____.

    (2)   The number which is 5 greater than -12 is_____.

    (3)   -3 is 6 less than _____.

    (4)   -10 is 6 greater than _____.

4. Calculate the following:

    (1)   (-4) + (+6)

    (2)   (-8) + (-13)

    (3)   (+1.1) + (-1.5)

    (4)   (+5) – (+7)

    (5)   (-3) – (-9)

    (6) $(-\frac{3}{7}) + (-\frac{2}{7})$

    (7) $(-\frac{3}{2}) - (-\frac{1}{4})$

    (8) $(+\frac{3}{4}) - (-\frac{1}{2})$

5. Calculate the following:

    (1)   0 – (-24) + (-5) – 7

    (2)   8 + (-12) – (-5)

    (3)   -2 + (-7) – (-9) – 6

    (4)   -12 + 13 + 8 – 9

    (5)   -5 – 3 + 9 – 11 – 2

    (6)   -7.2 – (+0.9) + (-1.6)

    (7)   0 – 2.4 – 8 + 13.4 – 6

    (8) $0 - (-\frac{1}{2}) - (+\frac{3}{4}) + (-1)$

    (9) $(-\frac{2}{3}) + (-\frac{1}{2}) - 1\frac{1}{6}$

    (10) $1 - (-\frac{2}{5}) + (-\frac{3}{10}) - (+0.1)$

6.   Calculate the following:

(1) $(+5) \times (-3)$

(2) $(-7) \times (-8)$

(3) $8 \times (-\frac{3}{4})$

(4) $(+10) \div (-2)$

(5) $(-4) \div (-\frac{2}{3})$

(6) $(-\frac{7}{6}) \div (+\frac{14}{9})$

(7) $(-4)^2 \times (-5)$

(8) $-(-2^3)$

(9) $8 \div (-\frac{2}{3})^2$

(10) $(-3) \times 6 - (-\frac{3}{4}) + \frac{3}{8}$

(11) $(-4) + (-3^2) \times (-2) + (-2) \times 5$

7.   Three people, A, B, and C, played cards. The total number of points they were able to
accumulate was 0. Using this information, answer the following questions:
(1)   If A has 8 points and C has -3 points, how many points does B have?
(2)   If the average of the points that A and B have accumulated is -6 points, how many
points does C have?

B

1.   Calculate the following:

(1) $15 - 3 \times \{7 - (-2)\}$

(2) $15 + (-2)^2 \times (-2^2)$

(3) $2^2 + (-1)^3 + 4 \times (-1)$

(4) $-2^2 \times 3 - (-3)^2 \times 5$

(5) $(-\frac{1}{3}) \times (-4) - (-\frac{1}{3})^2$

(6) $\frac{1}{12} \times (-3) - 6 + (-\frac{2}{3})$

(7) $2\frac{1}{3} - (-\frac{1}{2})^2 + (-\frac{3}{8})$

2.   Using inequality symbols, show the relations among the following groups of numbers:

(1) -5, $(-2)^2$, -3^2

(2) -0.03, $(-0.2)^3$, -0.1^2

3.   It is given that there are two numbers whose sum and product are both positive
numbers. What are the signs of those two numbers? Explain and give an example.

CHAPTER 3

LETTERS AND EXPRESSIONS

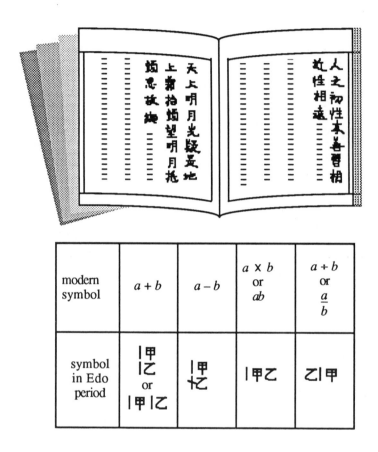

modern symbol	$a + b$	$a - b$	$a \times b$ or ab	$a + b$ or $\dfrac{a}{b}$
symbol in Edo period	甲 乙 or 甲 乙	甲 乙	甲乙	乙甲

In the first chart above, various symbols represent arithmetic operations. In the Second chart a and b and (ko) and (otsu) are letters used in place of numbers; they are not symbols for arithmetic operations. For example, a can represent various numbers such as 3, 4, or 5, and other letters can be used in the same way.

In the commutative law $a + b = b + a$ that you learned in the previous chapter, both a and b can be used to represent various numbers. There are numerous occasions when it is convenient to use letters in place of numbers, but there are many rules for writing expressions using letters.

1 USE OF LETTERS

 Numbers and Letters

Problem 1 When you buy one, two, or three 50-yen stamps, how much do you have to pay in each case? Write an expression to find the amount of money needed in each case.

The price of the stamps is

(price of one) x (number of stamps).

50	x	1	=	50
50	x	2	=	100
50	x	3	=	150
⋮		⋮		⋮
50	x	b		

If we use the letter b instead of the numbers that express the number of stamps bought

1, 2, 3, ...

then we can express the amount of money needed to buy b 50-yen stamps as

a x b

$(50 \times b)$ yen.

Further, we can express the amount of money needed to buy 5 stamps costing a yen per stamp as

$(a \times 5)$ yen

and we can express the amount of money needed to buy b stamps costing a yen per stamp as

$(a \times b)$ yen.

Example 1 Since we can find the perimeter of a square from

(the length of one side) x 4,

the perimeter of a square where one side equals a cm is

$(a \times 4)$ cm.

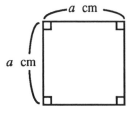

Problem 2 Express the following quantities with expressions using letters.

(1) The money needed to buy a meters of cloth at 500 yen per meter.

(2) The perimeter of an equilateral triangle in which one side equals x cm.

Example 2 When you buy something that costs a yen with a 1000-yen note, the change will be $(1000 - a)$ yen.

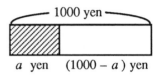

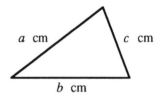

Example 3 When the three sides of a triangle are a cm, b cm, and c cm, the perimeter of the triangle is

$(a + b + c)$.

Problem 3 Solve the following problems:

(1) If the initial temperature is $a°$ C, how many degrees C will it be if the temperature goes up 3 degrees?

(2) 2 students are absent from a class of m students. How many students are present?

(3) A boy is x years old, and he is 4 years older than his younger brother. How old is the younger brother?

Problem 4 Which of the letters used in Problem 2 and Problem 3 stand for numbers that could include decimals? Which stand for numbers that could include negative numbers?

Rules for Using Letters

Expressions using letters usually appear in the following form:

Expressing Products

> **Expressing Products**
>
> (1) In multiplication that mixes in letters, the
>   x symbol is omitted.
>
> (2) In a product that mixes numbers and letters, write
>   the number in front of the letter.

Example 1 (1) $a \times b = ab$

(2) $a \times 3 = 3a$

(3) $a \times b \times c = abc$

(4) $(n - 5) \times 2 = 2(n - 5)$

(5) $(a + b) \times c = (a + b)c$

Note: Though $b \times a = ba$, in cases like this we write the product in alphabetical order, ab.

Problem 1 Write the following expressions, dropping the x symbol.

(1) $2 \times a$ (2) $c \times b$

(3) $x \times c \times 3$ (4) $(x - y) \times 3$

(5) $y \times (a + x)$ (6) $(a + b) \times (c + d)$

Problem 2   Write the following expressions that indicate quantities without using the x symbol.

(1)   4 times a (2)   5 times b

(3) m times a (4)   the sum of 2 times x and y

(5)   5 times the sum of a and b

Example 2   (1) $5a \times 3 = 5 \times a \times 3$

$$= 5 \times 3 \times a$$

$$= 15a$$

(2) $\frac{1}{2}x \times 2 = \frac{1}{2} \times x \times 2$

$$= \frac{1}{2} \times 2 \times x$$

$$= x$$

Note: $1 \times x$ and $x \times 1$ are not written $1x$ but simply x.

Problem 3   Simplify the following expressions as in Example 2:

(1) $3n \times 8$ (2) $a \times 1$

(3) $3 \times \frac{1}{3}y$ (4) $4x \times 5$

(5) $3 \times 7a$ (6) $0.2b \times 5$

The product of -5 and a, $(-5)a$, is written $-5a$.

The product of -1 and a, $(-1)a$, is not written $-1a$ but $-a$.

These are the items that change when you use the symbol a.

Example 3   (1) $(-2) \times 5a = (-2) \times 5 \times a$

$$= -10a$$

(2) $(-x) \times (-3) = (-1) \times x \times (-3)$

$$= 3x$$

(3) $(-4y) \times (-5) = (-4) \times y \times (-5)$

$$= 20y$$

Problem 4   Simplify the following expressions:

(1) $x \times (-4)$ (2) $15 \times (-a)$

(3) $(-b) \times (-1)$ (4) $(-0.4) \times (-2a)$

(5) $-(-2m)$ (6) $-(-3) \times \frac{3}{4}n$

Powers

As in the case of numbers, we write $a \times a$, or aa, as a^2, and we write $a \times a \times a$, or aaa, as a^3. The same is true of a^4, a^5, etc. We say that a^2, a^3 and the like are powers of a. The small 2 in a^2 and the small 3 in a^3 are called the exponents.

Example 4   (1) $xxyyy = x^2y^3$

(3) $(m + n)(m + n)(m + n) = (m + n)^3$

Problem 5   Write the following expressions using exponents:

(1) yyy (2) aab

(3) $3nnn$ (4) $(a + b)(a + b)$

Problem 6   Create expressions that represent the following quantities:

(1)   The area of a square with a side of a cm.

(2)   The volume of a cube with an edge of a cm.

Expressing Quotients

The quotient of $2 \div 3$ is $\frac{2}{3}$. In the same way, we write the quotient of $a \div b$ as $\frac{a}{b}$.

Expressing Quotients

When division includes letters, we do not use the $\div$ symbol but instead write the expression in the form of a fraction.

Example 5   (1) $a \div 5 = \frac{a}{5}$ (2) $3x \div 4 = \frac{3x}{4}$

(3) $(a + b) \div c = \frac{a + b}{c}$

Note: Since $a \div 5 = a \times \frac{1}{5}$, it can also be written as $\frac{1}{5}a$. Also, you can write $\frac{3x}{4}$ as $\frac{3}{4}x$.

Problem 7   Write the following expressions without the $\div$ symbol.

(1) $c \div 4$ (2) $3 \div x$ (3) $4a \div b$

(4) $(x + y) \div a$ (5) $c \div (x + y)$

Example 6 $a \div bc = \frac{a}{bc}$

Note: $a + bc$ signifies $a + (b \times c)$ and not $(a + b) \times c$.

Example 7   (1) $4a \div 6 = \dfrac{4a}{6}$ (2) $2a \div (-3) = \dfrac{2a}{-3}$

$\qquad\qquad\qquad\qquad = \dfrac{2a}{3}$ $\qquad\qquad\qquad\qquad = -\dfrac{2a}{3}$

Problem 8   Simplify the following expressions:

(1) $x \div 2a$ (2) $a \div (-5)$ (3) $3y \div 6$

(4) $x \div ab$ (5) $(-9a) \div 6$ (6) $(-4x) \div (-2)$

Problem 9   Indicate the meaning of the following expressions, using the symbols $\times$ and $\div$:

(1) $\dfrac{ab}{3}$ (2) $4x^2$ (3) $\dfrac{a-b}{x}$ (4) $\dfrac{5}{x+y}$

Example 8   Write the following expressions without using the symbols $\times$ or $\div$:

(1) $a \div b - c$ (2) $a \times b \div c$

[Solution]   (1) $a \div b - c = \dfrac{a}{b} - c$ (2) $a \times b \div = \dfrac{ab}{c}$

Problem 10   Simplify the following expressions as in Example 8:

(1) $b \div c \times a$ (2) $a - b \div c$

(3) $a \times 2 - b$ (4) $a \div b \times c$

Expressing Quantities

You have already learned on pages 55 and 56 how to express quantities that include letters, such as "(50 × *b*) yen", but here we will express them without the × and the ÷.

Example 1   If you buy *b* products that cost *a* yen each and pay for them with a 1,000-yen note, how much change will you get?

[Solution]   The change is 1,000 yen − (the cost of what you bought), that is, 1,000 yen − (the price of one) × (number bought)

or   (1,000 − *a* × *b*) yen

or, simplified,   (1,000 − *ab*) yen.

Answer: (1,000 − *ab*) yen

Problem 1   Write the following quantities as expressions using variables:

(1)   The money used to buy *b* meters of a cloth that costs *a* yen per meter.

(2)   A person walked a path 12 km long for *a* hours at a speed of 4 km per hour. Express the remaining distance.

Example 2   See the diagram at the right. If you join two sticks each *a* cm long with 3 sticks each *b* cm long, how long, in centimeters, would the entire stick be?

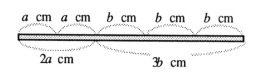

a cm *a* cm   *b* cm   *b* cm   *b* cm

2*a* cm   3*b* cm

[Solution]   *a* × 2 + *b* × 3 = 2*a* + 3*b*

Answer: (2*a* + 3*b*) cm

Problem 2 Solve the following problems:

(1) What is the total amount of money you need to buy a 20-yen stamps and b 50-yen stamps?

(2) If you buy 10 pencils at x yen each and 5 note pads at y yen each, how much money will you need to buy both?

Example 3 How many minutes does it take to travel a distance of b m at a speed of a m/minute?

[Solution] (time taken) = (distance) ÷ (speed)

Thus, the time taken is

$$b \div a \ = \ \frac{b}{a} \text{ (minutes)}$$

Answer: $\frac{b}{a}$ minutes

Problem 3 Write the following quantities with expressions using variables:

(1) What is the price of one orange if you pay 200 yen for a oranges?

(2) If it takes c hours to walk a km, what is the speed in kilometers per hour?

Problem 4 1 meter equals how many centimeters? How many centimeters are there in a meters?

Example 4 If you use cm as the units, the sum of a m and b cm is expressed as

$$(100a + b) \text{ cm}$$

If you use meters as the units, the sum of a m and b cm is expressed as

$$(a + \frac{b}{100}) \text{m}$$

When you write the sum or difference of quantities given in two or more different units in one expression, you have to keep the units constant.

Problem 5   Show the sum of the following quantities using the units written in the parentheses to the right:

(1)   4 cm and y mm (mm)   (2) x min and y sec (sec)

(3) a hours and b min (hours)   (4) a kg and b g (kg)

Problem 6   When you cut 7 pieces of string a cm long from a string l m long, how many centimeters remain?

Example 5   How many grams are $p\%$ of 600 g?

[Solution]   Since $p\%$ equals $\dfrac{p}{100}$, $p\%$ of 600g is

$$600 \times \frac{p}{100} = 6p \ (g)$$

Answer: $6p$ g

Problem 7   Solve the following problems:

(1)   How many yen is a wari (1 wari = 10%) of 100 yen?

(2)   How many meters is $b\%$ of a m?

Exercises

1.   Simplify the following expressions:

(1) $x \times 5$ (2) $c \times b \times 4$ (3) $(a - b) \times 3$

(4) $l \times (-1)$ (5) $3 + 5y$ (6) $2x + (-3)$

(7) $(-9a) + 3$

2.   Make up expressions to represent the following quantities.

(1)   2 wari (1 wari = 10%) of *a* yen.

(2)   The average of *m* and *n*.

(3)   The square of the sum of *x* and *a*.

(4)   The remainder when *a* is divided by *b* and the quotient is 5.

(5)   The positive two-digit integers whose tens place and ones place are *a* and *b*, respectively.

3.   In the diagram to the right, indicate the lengths of *AD*, *CX*, and *CD* with expressions using the letters *l*, *a*, and *b*.

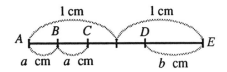

EXPRESSIONS WITH LETTERS, AND CALCULATIONS WITH THEM

Substitution and the Value of an Expression

The price of m pencils at 50 yen apiece and n erasers at 40 yen apiece can be expressed as

$$(50m + 40n) \text{ yen.}$$

Similarly, you can find out how much money you need to buy 6 pencils and 2 erasers by inserting 6 and 2 in place of the letters m and n. That is, if $m = 6$ and $n = 2$, then

$$
\begin{array}{ccccccccc}
50 & \times & (m) & + & 40 & \times & (n) & & \\
| & & | & & | & & | & & \\
50 & \times & 6 & + & 40 & \times & 2 & = & 380 \text{ (yen)}
\end{array}
$$

Also, the money you need to buy 3 pencils and 5 erasers becomes:

$$50 \times 3 + 40 \times 5 = 350 \quad \text{(yen)}$$

This kind of replacement of variables with numbers in an expression is called **substitution**, and the result which is calculated after substitution is called the **value of an expression**.

Example 1   When $a = 5$ and $b = -2$, calculate the value of $2a + 3b$ as shown on the right.

$$
\begin{aligned}
2a + 3b &= 2 \times 5 + 3 \times (-2) \\
&= 10 + (-6) \\
&= 4
\end{aligned}
$$

Problem 1   Find the value of the following expressions for $a = 2$ and $b = -3$:

(1) $3a + 4b$ 　　　(2) $2a - 5b$ 　　　(3) $a + \dfrac{1}{3}b$

Example 2   When $a = -4$, if you want to find the value of a^2 and $-a^2$,

$$a^2 = (-4)^2 \qquad\qquad -a^2 = -(-4)^2$$
$$= 16 \qquad\qquad\qquad = -(+16)$$
$$\qquad\qquad\qquad\qquad = -16$$

Problem 2   Find the value of the following expressions for $a = -3$:

(1) $-a$ (2) a^2 (3) $-4a^2$ (4) $(-a)^2$

Example 3   Find the value of the following expressions for $x = 5$ and $y = -6$:

(1) $x^2 - y^2$ (2) $2x^2 - 3xy$

[Solution]   (1) $x^2 - y^2 = 5^2 - (-6)^2$

$$= 25 - (+36)$$
$$= 25 - 36$$
$$= -11$$

(2) $2x^2 - 3xy = 2 \times 5^2 - 3 \times 5 \, (-6)$

$$= 50 - (-90)$$
$$= 50 + 90$$
$$= 140$$

Answers: (1) -11   (2) 140

Problem 3   Find the value of the following expressions for $a = -5$ and $b = 4$:

(1) $\dfrac{1}{2}\,ab$ (2) $(-a)^2 b$ (3) $-3a^2 + 2ab$

Problem 4   In the following cases, find the value of $6x - y^2$:

(1) $x = -2, y = 5$ (2) $x = \frac{1}{2}, y = -1$

 2   ## Calculating Linear Expressions

Expressions, Terms, and Coefficients

Problem 1   Write expressions to show
the area and the perimeter
of a rectangle with a height
of a cm and a width of
b cm.

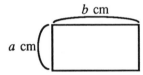

Let us look at expressions that combine variables and numbers in addition, subtraction, multiplication, or division as in $ab, 2a + 2b$, and $\frac{a-b}{2}$.

In an expression such as $3x - 2y$, where

$$3x - 2y = 3x + (-2y),$$

it is possible to show the form of the sum of $3x$ and $-2y$.

When you convert expressions that combine
addition and subtraction to expressions involving
only addition, the numbers joined by the addition
symbol, such as

$3x, -2y,$

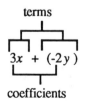

are called **terms**. Also, the numerical parts, 3 and -2, of terms like $3x$ and $-2y$ are called **coefficients**.

Example 1 (1)   The terms of $-3x + 2y$ are: $-3x,$ $2y.$

(2)   The terms of $x^2 - 4x - 3$ are: $x^2,$ $-4x,$ $-3.$

Problem 2 Find the terms and coefficients in the following expressions:

(1) $4a - b$ (2) $x + 6y$ (3) $7x^2 - 4x$

Linear Expressions

An expression written in a form where a number other than 0 is multiplied by one variable and then added to one number, as in $2x + 5$, is called a **linear expression.**

Example 2 Since $2x - 3$ consists of a variable x multiplied by 2 and added to -3, and since $-4y$ can be thought of as y multiplied by -4 and added to 0, both are linear expressions.

Problem 3 Which of the following are linear expressions?

(1) $2a + 3$ (2) $-3b + 4$ (3) $5x$ (4) x^2 (5) $-y$

Multiplication with Numbers

If we use the distributive law, we can form expressions with no parentheses from expressions that have parentheses.

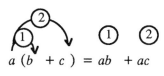
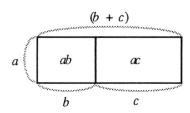

Example 3   (1) $4(x + 3)$ $= 4 \times x + 4 \times 3$

$= 4x + 12$

(2) $-2(3x - 5)$ $= (-2) \times 3x + (-2) \times (-5)$

$= -6x + 10$

(3) $(8a - 6) \times \dfrac{1}{2}$ $= 8a \times \dfrac{1}{2} - 6 \times \dfrac{1}{2}$

$= 4a - 3$

Problem 4   Perform the following calculations:

(1) $3(a - 4)$ (2) $5(2a - 3)$ (3) $-2(c + 5)$

(4) $-4(3x - 5)$ (5) $\dfrac{2}{3}(x - 6)$ (6) $(\dfrac{2}{3}x - \dfrac{1}{4}) \times 24$

Example 4 $\dfrac{2x + 1}{3} \times 6 = \dfrac{(2x + 1) \times \overset{2}{\cancel{6}}}{\underset{1}{\cancel{3}}}$

$= (2x + 1) \times 2$

$= 4x + 2$

Problem 5   Perform the following calculations:

(1) $\dfrac{x + 1}{4} \times 12$ (2) $\dfrac{5x - 3}{3} \times 9$ (3) $\dfrac{2x + 5}{7} \times 14$

Like Terms

Terms in which the variable is the same we call **like terms**, as in the $3x$ and $4x$ and the $5y$ and $-3y$ of

$$3x + 5y + 4x - 3y$$

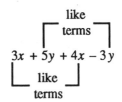

If we use the distributive law, like terms can be combined in the following way.

$$3x + 4x \quad = (3 + 4)x \quad = 7x$$

$$5y - 3y \quad = (5 - 3)y \quad = 2y$$

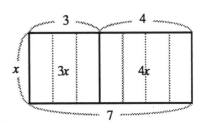

(Problem 6)   Perform the following calculations:

(1) $5x + 7x$ (2) $6y - 2y$ (3) $4x - 3x$

(4) $-2a + 6a$ (5) $3y - y$ (6) $7a + (-8a)$

Even in expressions with numerous terms, we can combine like terms as we did above.

(Example 5)   (1) $7x - 3 - 5x + 6$ (2) $\dfrac{a}{2} + 3 - \dfrac{a}{3} - 4$

$$= 7x - 5x - 3 + 6 \qquad\qquad = \dfrac{a}{2} - \dfrac{a}{3} + 3 - 4$$

$$= (7 - 5x)x + (-3 + 6) \qquad = \dfrac{3}{6}a - \dfrac{2}{6}a + 4 - 4$$

$$= 2x + 3 \qquad\qquad\qquad\qquad = \dfrac{a}{6} - 1$$

(Problem 7)   Perform the following calculations:

(1) $6a - 4a - 5a$ (2) $7x - 11x + 3x$

(3) $3x - 2 + x$ (4) $a + 5 - 7a - 2$

(5) $\dfrac{a}{2} + 5 - \dfrac{a}{4} - 3$ (6) $\dfrac{m}{3} + 3 - m - \dfrac{1}{3}$

Addition and Subtraction of Linear Expressions

Example 6 Try adding $3a + 2$ and $4a - 5$.

$$(3a + 2) + (4a - 5) = 3a + 2 + 4a - 5$$
$$= 3a + 4a + 2 - 5$$
$$= 7a - 3$$

$$\begin{array}{r} 3a + 2 \\ +) \ 4a - 5 \\ \hline 7a - 3 \end{array}$$

Problem 8 Perform the following calculations:

(1) $(4a - 3) + (5a + 6)$ (2) $(2x + 5) + (3x - 7)$

(3) $(7 - 2a) + (3a - 6)$ (4) $(2 - a) + (6 - 9a)$

Subtraction is equivalent to changing the sign and adding.

To change the sign, multiply by -1. For example,

$$-(3a - 4) = (-1)(3a - 4) = -3a + 4$$

Using this method, we can subtract linear expressions as follows:

Example 7 $(a + 7) - (5a - 3)$

$$= a + 7 + (-5a + 3)$$
$$= a + 7 - 5a + 3$$
$$= -4a + 10$$

$$\begin{array}{r} a + 7 \\ -) \ 5a - 3 \\ \hline -4a + 10 \end{array} \qquad \begin{array}{r} a + 7 \\ +) \ -5a + 3 \\ \hline -4a + 10 \end{array}$$

Problem 9 Perform the following calculations:

(1) $(9a - 7) - (2a + 3)$ (2) $(a + 10) - (2a - 1)$

(3) $(5a + 4) - (-4a + 7)$ (4) $(2a - 9) - (-5a - 3)$

Various Calculations

Example 8   Calculate $2(x + 3) - 3(2x - 1)$.

〖 Approach 〗   Apply the distributive law, write expressions without parentheses, and combine the like terms.

〖 Solution 〗

$$2(x + 3) - 3(2x - 1) = 2x + 6 - 6x + 3$$
$$= -4x + 9$$

Answer: $-4x + 9$

Problem 10   Perform the following calculations:

(1) $6(x + 2) + 5(2x - 3)$ (2) $-3(x - 4) + 2(x + 5)$

(3) $2(x - 7) - 4(-x + 2)$ (4) $5(3x - 2) - 4(3 - x)$

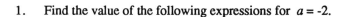

Exercises

1.   Find the value of the following expressions for $a = -2$.

(1) $3 - a$ (2) $-a^2 - 1$

2.   Find the value of the following expressions for $a = 3$ and $b = -5$.

(1) $-b$ (2) $-b^2$ (3) $a - b$

(4) $2a - 3b$ (5) $a^2 - ab + 3$

3.   Perform the following calculations:

(1) $6x - 8x$

(2) $-2a + 3a - 5a$

(3) $x - 5 - 3x + 8$

(4) $4a - a + 7 - \dfrac{7}{3}a - 2$

(5) $(-2a - 4) + (4 - 2a)$

(6) $(3 - 2a) - (7a - 5)$

(7) $2(x - 3) - (x + 5)$

(8) $\dfrac{x - 4}{4} \times 12 - \dfrac{x - 1}{6} \times 12$

4.   What is the perimeter of a rectangle whose width is 4 cm and whose height is a cm less than the width? How many square centimeters is the area?

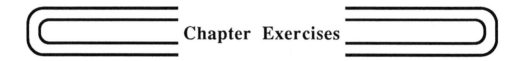

Chapter Exercises

A

1.   Simplify the following expressions:

(1) $ab \times (-1)$

(2) $-(-5) + 1$

(3) $a \times 5 - 8 \times b$

(4) $a + b \times (-2)$

(5) $s \times s \times s + t \times t$

(6) $(x + 1) \times (x + 2) \times (x + 2)$

2.   Find the value of the following expressions for $a = -2$, $b = 3$, and $c = -1$.

(1) $2a - 3b - 4c$

(2) $a^2 + bc - c^2$

3.   Perform the following calculations:

(1) $2x + 3x$

(2) $6y - 7y$

(3) $-2.7x - 4.3x$

(4) $\dfrac{x}{2} - \dfrac{x}{3} + \dfrac{x}{4}$

(5) $4x - 7 + 2x + 6$

(6) $3y - 6 - 5y + 8$

(7) $(3x - 2) + (4x + 7)$

(8) $(-2a - 4) - (4 - 2a)$

(9) $3(2a - 3) - 4(a - 5)$

(10) $\dfrac{x - 3}{2} \times 8 + (3x - 5)$

B

1.   Answer the following questions:

(1)   What is the perimeter of a regular hexagon with a side of x cm?

(2)   How much money does it take to buy a 20-yen stamps and b 30-yen stamps?

(3)   After we have divided x sheets of paper among 20 children, giving each b sheets, how many sheets remain?

(4)   How much is a percent of 2000 yen?

(5)   How much is x% of a g?

(6)   Last year there were x students at a certain school. This year the number of students increased by p% over last year. How many students are there this year?

CHAPTER 4

EQUATIONS

It is said that the ancient Greek mathematician Diophantus (ca. 3rd century) was the first to use expressions containing letters.

The following is a translation of a poem about Diophantus' life. "$\frac{1}{6}$ of Diophantus' life was his youth, and then it took $\frac{1}{12}$ of his life to lengthen his beard. After another $\frac{1}{7}$ of his life he got married, and 5 years later a child was born. This child left the world 4 years earlier than half the span of his father's years."

If you consider Diophantus' life to be x years, from the diagram below you can obtain these expressions,

$$\frac{1}{6}x + \frac{1}{12}x + \frac{1}{7}x + 5 + \frac{1}{2}x + 4 = x$$

and you find that $x = 84$.

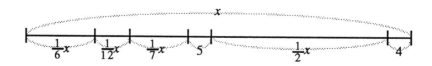

1 EQUATIONS

1 Equalities

If we cut x pieces of rope 2 m long from a rope of length a m, there will be 5 m left. In this case, we can write an expression

$a - 2x = 5$

to show the relation between a and x.
This relation can also be expressed as
$a = 2x + 5$.

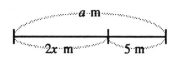

An expression which shows the relation between quantities forming an equation is called an **equality**. In an equality, the part to the left of the equal sign is called the **left side**, and the part to the right of the equal sign is called the **right side**. When the left side and the right side are taken together we speak of the **two sides**.

equality

$$\underset{\text{left side}}{a} = \underset{\text{right side}}{2x + 5}$$

two sides

Problem 1   In $a - 2x = 5$, indicate the left side and the right side.

Problem 2   Use equalities to express the relations between the quantities in the following situations.

(1)   If you cut 2 pieces of tape x cm long from a piece of tape 60 cm long, the remainder is a cm.

(2)   The distance walked is r km if you walk at a rate of 4 km/hour for t hours.

(3)   There are a pencils. If you give 3 pencils to each of b people, you will be two pencils short.

Example 1   Let us write an
equation that shows
the relation between
x and y in the
parallelogram to the
right.

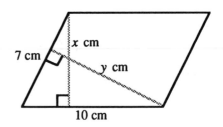

(Area of a parallelogram) = (base) × (height)

If we take the 10 cm side as the base, then the height can be regarded
as x cm, and if we take the 7 cm side as the base, then the height can
be expressed as y cm. Thus,

$$10x = 7y$$

Problem 3   Write an equality that
expresses the relation
between x and y in
the right triangle
depicted at the right.

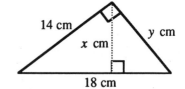

Equations

"If you multiply a certain number by 3 and add 4, this is equivalent to multiplying the
original number by 5." This relation can be written with the following expression, if you
represent the original number as x.

$$3x + 4 = 5x \tag{1}$$

Depending on what number you insert in equation (1) for x, it may be true or it may
be false.

Example 2   Let us replace x with 0, 1, 2, 3, 4, and see if equation (1) is true or
not.

value of x	left side	right side	$3x + 4 = 5x$
0	3 × 0 + 4 = 4	5 × 0 = 0	is not true
1	3 × 1 + 4 = 7	5 × 1 = 5	is not true
2	3 × 2 + 4 = 10	5 × 2 = 10	is true
3	3 × 3 + 4 = 13	5 × 3 = 15	is not true
4	3 × 4 + 4 = 16	5 × 4 = 20	is not true

(1) is true when x is replaced by 2. We say that a valid equality which results from substituting certain numbers for the variables in an expression is an **equation**. Also, when a number is substituted and validates an equation, that number is referred to as the **solution** to the equation. For example, 2 is the solution to equation (1).

Problem 4 Which of the following equations have 4 as their solution?

(1) $2x + 5 = 10$ (2) $3x - 8 = x$

(3) $\frac{1}{2}x + 3 = 2x - 3$ (4) $2(x - 1) = 3x - 5$

Problem 5 Choose the solutions to the following equations from among -1, 0 and 1:

(1) $3x - 5 = x - 3$ (2) $4x + 3 = -x - 2$

Exercises

1. Express each of the following relations in an equation:

(1) The sum of a number x times 2 plus 8 is equal to 4 times the sum of x and 3.

(2 $\frac{1}{4}$ of a number a minus 6 is equal to $\frac{1}{10}$ of a.

(3) There are x students in class A. There are three more students in class B than in A, and the total number of students in classes A and B is 75.

2. Express in words the relations in the following equations.

(1) $x + 3 = -5$

(2) $2x + 6 = 14$

(3) $6(x - 2) = x - 7$

SOLVING EQUATIONS

 Properties of Equalities

When balancing two scales we can make the following observations.

A balanced scale will remain balanced even if two objects of the same weight are added to both sides or if two objects of the same weight are taken away.

Also, a balanced scale will remain balanced even when equal multiples of objects are added or are taken away.

The properties of an equality can be thought of in the same way.

Generally, equalities have the following properties.

Properties of Equalities

(1)   If you add the same numbers to both sides of an equality, it will remain valid.

If $A = B$, then $A + C = B + C$

(2)   If you subtract the same numbers from both sides of an equality, it will remain valid.

If $A = B$, then $A - C = B - C$

---

(3)   If both sides of an equality are multiplied by the same number, the equality will remain valid.

$$\text{If } A = B, \text{ then } AC = BC$$

(4)   If both sides of an equality are divided by the same number, the equality will remain valid, provided that $C \neq 0$.

$$\text{If } A = B, \text{ then } \frac{A}{C} = \frac{B}{C}$$

Also,

(5)   if the sides of an equality are transposed, the equality will remain valid.

$$\text{If } A = B, \text{ then } B = A$$

This can be thought of as equivalent to the way that a balanced scale will remain balanced when all the objects on both sides are transposed.

Problem 1   In (1) and (2) below, you can utilize the properties of equalities to transform the upper equality into the lower equality. Explain the method of performing this transformation. Also, explain the method of transforming the lower equality into the upper equality.

(1) $\begin{cases} a + 3 = 5 \\ a = 5 - 3 \end{cases}$ (2) $\begin{cases} 3x = 6 \\ x = 2 \end{cases}$

  The Properties of Equalities and Solving Equations

Finding the solution to an equation is referrered to as **solving** the equation. By using the properties of equalities to transform the equation, you can solve the equation.

Example 1   Solve $x + 9 = 4$.

In order to isolate x on the left side, subtract 9 from both sides:

$$x + 9 - 9 = 4 - 9.$$

You get $x = -5.$

If you substitute -5 back into the original equation $x + 9 = 4$,

$$\text{the left side equals } -5 + 9 = 4,$$
$$\text{and the right side equals } 4.$$

Therefore, the equation is valid.

This example demonstrates that the solution to the equation $x + 9 = 4$ is -5. This means that $x = -5$.

(Problem 1) Solve the following equations:

(1) $x + 4 = 12$ (2) $10 + x = 7$ (3) $y - 7 = 6$

(Example 2) Solve $4x = 6$.

In order to make the coefficient of x equal 1, divide each side by 4.

$$\frac{4x}{4} = \frac{6}{4}$$

Thus, $x = \dfrac{3}{2}$

(Problem 2) Check whether $\dfrac{3}{2}$ is the solution to the equation $4x = 6$.

(Problem 3) Solve the following equations:

(1) $2x = 16$ (2) $3x = -9$ (3) $4 = 6y$

(Example 3) Solve $-2x = 8$.

If you divide both sides of the equation by -2,

$$\frac{-2x}{-2} = \frac{8}{-2}$$

then $x = -4$.

Problem 4 Check whether -4 is the solution to the equation $-2x = 8$.

Problem 5 Solve the following equations:

(1) $-9x = 27$ (2) $-6x = 15$ (3) $-21 = -14x$

Example 4 Solve $\frac{2}{3}x = 8$ using two different methods.

(1) In order to make the coefficient of x equal 1, multiply both sides by $\frac{3}{2}$, the reciprocal of $\frac{2}{3}$,

$$\frac{2}{3}x \times \frac{3}{2} = 8 \times \frac{3}{2}$$

$$x = 12$$

(2) First multiply both sides by 3, and then divide both sides by 2.

$$\frac{2}{3}x \times 3 = 8 \times 3$$

$$2x = 24$$

$$x = 12$$

Problem 6 Check whether 12 is the solution to the equation $\frac{2}{3}x = 8$.

Problem 7 Solve the following equations:

(1) $\frac{x}{2} = 8$ (2) $\frac{3}{4}x = -\frac{9}{2}$ (3) $-\frac{2}{3}x = \frac{5}{7}$

Drills

1. Solve the following equations:

(1) $x + 8 = 2$ (2) $-2 = y - 5$ (3) $5y = 3$

(4) $-7x = 21$ (5) $\frac{3}{5}x = -9$ (6) $-\frac{12}{25} = -\frac{8}{5}x$

Solving Linear Equations

You can use properties (1) and (2) of equalities that you learned above in the following ways.

If you add b to both sides of $a - b = c$, you get $a = c + b$.

If you subtract b from both sides of $a + b = c$, you get $a = c - b$.

In these instances, moving the terms $-b$ and $+b$ from the left side of the equalities $a - b = c$ and $a + b = c$ can be thought of as moving them to the right side by changing their respective signs.

Generally, terms on one side of an equality can be moved to the other side by changing their signs. We call this **transposing terms**.

Example 1   (1)   In the equation
$x + 9 = 4$, if you
transpose the term 9,

$$x = 4 - 9$$

$$x + 9 = 4$$

$$x = 4 - \underline{9}$$

Thus, $x = -5$

(2)   In the equation
$2x = 15 - 3x$, if you
transpose the term $-3x$,

$$2x + 3x = 15$$

$$2x = 15 - \underline{3x}$$

$$2x + \underline{3x} = 15$$

If you then simplify,

$$5x = 15,$$

and divide each side by 5,

$$x = 3.$$

By transposing terms and simplifying, you can arrive at equations of the form

(linear expression) $= 0$,

and these are called **linear equations**.

For example, equation (1) of Example 1 can be transformed into

$$x + 5 = 0,$$

and equation (2) can be transformed into

$$5x - 15 = 0,$$

so that the left sides of both become linear expressions, and both are linear equations.

(Problem 1) Solve the following equations:

       (1) $4x - 7 = 1$ (2) $3x = 4 - x$ (3) $9 - 2x = x$

(Example 2) Solve $9x - 5 = 2x + 23$.

[Approach]   Put terms that include x on the left side and terms that do not include x on the right side.

[Solution]   If you transpose the term -5, then

$$9x = 2x + 23 + 5,$$

and if you transpose $2x$ to the left side and simplify, then

$$9x - 2x = 23 + 5$$

$$7x = 28$$

Then divide both sides by 7:

$$x = 4$$

                  Answer: $x = 4$

[Check]   The left side   = 9 x 4 – 5 = 31
                  The right side   = 2 x 4 + 23 = 31

We can write the solution as follows:

[Solution]   If we change terms and simplify,

$$9x - 2x = 23 + 5$$
$$7x = 28$$
$$x = 4$$

                  Answer: $x = 4$

Note: Henceforth, checks will not be given in this textbook.

Problem 2 Solve the following equations:

(1) $2x + 7 = 19 - 4x$ (2) $9 - x = 2 + 6x$

(3) $5x + 8 = 2x - 4$ (4) $8x - 10 = 9x - 4$

(5) $6 + 10y = 3y - 1$ (6) $-7x + 1 = -x + 1$

Example 3 Solve $5x - 2(x - 1) = 14$.

[**Solution**] If you eliminate the parentheses, then

$$5x - 2x + 2 = 14$$

If you simplify and transpose terms, then

$$5x - 2x = 14 - 2$$

$$3x = 12$$

$$x = 4$$

Answer: $x = 4$

Problem 3 Solve the following equations:

(1) $4(x + 4) + 1 = 65$ (2) $7x - 3(x - 1) = 23$

(3) $6x - 9(2 - x) = 12$ (4) $3 = 1 - (8 - 2x)$

(5) $5(x - 3) - 8(-2 + x) = -5$

Example 4 Solve $\frac{1}{2}x - 4 = \frac{1}{5}x + 2$.

[Approach] First, in order to simplify the coefficients of x, multiply both sides by the least common multiple of 2 and 5. Next, separate the terms which contain x from those terms which are numbers.

[**Solution**] If you multiply both sides by 10, then

$$\frac{1}{2}x \times 10 - 4 \times 10 = \frac{1}{5}x \times 10 + 2 \times 10$$

$$5x - 40 = 2x + 20$$

and if you transpose terms,

$$5x - 2x = 20 + 40$$

$$3x = 60$$

$$x = 20$$

Answer: $x = 20$

As in Example 4, if you have an equation with fractional coefficients, multiply both sides by a common multiple of the denominator. When you have the equation in a form without fractions, go ahead and solve it.

We refer to this kind of transformation as **clearing the fractions**. If, as in this case, the least common multiple of denominators is easy to find, it is simplest to use it.

Problem 4 Solve the following equations:

(1) $2x + \frac{1}{3} = \frac{x}{3} + 2$ (2) $\frac{8}{7}x - 6 = \frac{2}{3}x + 4$

(3) $\frac{2}{5}x + 6 = \frac{4}{3} - x$ (4) $\frac{3}{4} - \frac{y}{2} = -\frac{2}{5}y + 1$

Example 5 Solve $\frac{x + 3}{6} - \frac{2x - 3}{4} = 2$.

[**Solution**] If you remove the denominator by multiplying both sides by 12, then

$$\left(\frac{x + 3}{6}\right) \times 12 - \left(\frac{2x - 3}{4}\right) \times 12 = 2 \times 12$$

$$2(x + 3) - 3(2x - 3) = 24$$

If you eliminate the parentheses, then

$$2x + 6 - 6x + 9 = 24.$$

If you transpose the terms, then

$$2x - 6x = 24 - 6 - 9$$

$$-4x = 9$$

$$x = -\frac{9}{4}$$

Answer: $x = -\frac{9}{4}$

Note: $\dfrac{x+3}{6} - \dfrac{2x-3}{4} = 2$ can be written as $\dfrac{1}{6}(x+3) - \dfrac{1}{4}(2x-3) = 2$.

Problem 5 Solve the following equations:

(1) $\dfrac{2x-1}{3} = \dfrac{x+3}{2}$　(2) $\dfrac{2x-3}{3} + \dfrac{3x-4}{5} = 2$

(3) $x - \dfrac{x-1}{4} = -5$　(4) $\dfrac{1}{5}(2x-1) + \dfrac{1}{2}(x+7) = 6$

Example 6 Solve $0.7x + 1.37 = 1.5x - 0.23$.

[Solution] If you multiply both sides by 100, then

$$70x + 137 = 150x - 23$$

$$70x - 150x = -23 - 137$$

$$-80x = -160$$

$$x = 2$$

Answer: $x = 2$

As in Example 6, if you have an equation with decimal coefficients, multiply both sides by a power of 10, and you can solve it after converting it into a form without decimals.

Problem 6 Solve the following equations:

(1) $0.5x - 3 = 5.5$

(2) $0.25x - 0.04 = 0.26$

We can summarize the methods of solving linear equations in the following way.

Methods of Solving Linear Equations

(1)   When an equation involves fractional or decimal coefficients, convert them into integers. And if there are parentheses, eliminate them.

(2)   Isolate the terms with variables on one side of the equation and the numerical terms on the other side.

(3)   If there are terms that you can combine, combine them and then simplify them. Then write them in the form $ax = b$.

(4)   Divide both sides by the coefficient a of x. The answer will be $x = \dfrac{b}{a}$.

Drills

1.   Solve the following equations:

(1) $5x - 8 = 80 - 6x$

(2) $-3m - 10 = 14 - m$

(3) $3(x - 7) = 5(3 - x) - 4$

(4) $0.5x - 0.8 = 0.3x$

(5) $\dfrac{1}{2}x + \dfrac{1}{2} = \dfrac{1}{3} - \dfrac{1}{3}x$

(6) $\dfrac{3x + 4}{3} - \dfrac{2x - 3}{5} = 2$

 Applying Linear Equations

Let's solve the following problem by applying linear equations.

The price of a box of 15 apples is 950 yen, of which the box itself costs 50 yen. How much does one apple cost?

In order to express this problem as an equation we let x represent the price of one apple. Then the price of 15 apples will be $15x$.

Thus,

(price of apples) + (price of box) = (price of 1 box of apples)

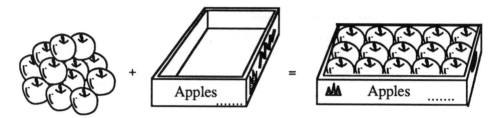

This problem can be expressed as the following equation:

$$15x + 50 = 950$$

If you solve this equation, then

$$x = 60$$

Therefore, one apple costs 60 yen.

(Problem 1) A man weighs 66 kg, and he is 1.5 times heavier than his son. How much does the son weigh?

For this problem state what x represents, and write an equation. Solve the equation and give the answer.

(Example 1) We cut a rope 3 m long into two pieces, and call one piece A and the other piece B. A is 8 cm longer than B. How long are A and B respectively?

〚 Approach 〛

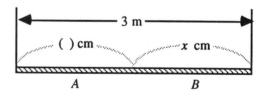

If we let x cm represent the length of B, then the length of A will equal $(x + 8)$ cm.

Further,

(length of A) + (length of B) $=$ 300 (cm)

Express this relationship as an equation, and solve it.

Note: Be sure to maintain equal units on both sides when you represent a problem with an equation.

[Solution]   If we let x represent the length of B, then

$$(x + 8) + x = 300$$

$$2x = 292$$

$$x = 146$$

The length of rope A is

$$146 + 8 = 154 \text{ (cm)}$$

Answer: A 154 cm, B 146 cm

Problem 2   This time do Example 1 by letting x be the length of rope A.

Problem 3   We would like to form a rectangle whose perimeter is 11 cm and whose length is 5 mm longer than its width. How many centimeters should the width be?

To solve word problems by making up equations, carry out the following steps.

Applying Equations

(1)   First completely understand the meaning of the word problem, and then decide what to express with x.

(2)   Express the relation between the quantities with an equation.

(3)   Solve the equation that you created and find the answer.

Example 2   15 minutes after a steamship leaves port a motorboat sets out after it. If the speed of the steamship is 200 m/minute and the speed of the motorboat is 500 m/minute, how long will the motorboat take to catch the steamship?

[Approach]   If we let x represent the time that the motorboat takes to catch the steamship, then the distance from the port to where the boat meets the ship can be expressed in the following two ways.

(1)   In the case of the motorboat, the distance is

$$500x \text{ m} \qquad\qquad (1)$$

(2)   In the case of the steamship, the distance is

$$200(15 + x) \text{ m} \qquad\qquad (2)$$

Combine (1) and (2) with an equal sign to form an equation.

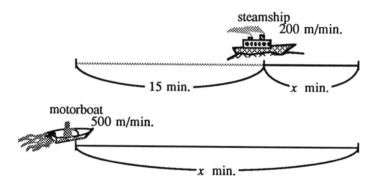

Problem 4   Make up an equation that describes the situation above and solve it.

Problem 5   15 minutes after a boy leaves home, his younger brother sets out after him on his bicycle. If the older brother's speed is 100 m/minute and the younger brother's speed is 300 m/minute, how long will it take for the younger brother to catch the older brother?

Exercises

1. Solve the following equations:

   (1) $y + 75 = 5$ (2) $x - 10 = 3$

   (3) $6 - x = 2$ (4) $\frac{1}{6}x = 9$

   (5) $-5x = \frac{1}{3}$ (6) $-\frac{x}{2} = \frac{1}{8}$

   (7) $9x + 4 = 7$ (8) $3x - 4 = 16$

   (9) $7 - 4x = 35$ (10) $-6 - 2x = -4$

2. Solve the following equations:

   (1) $7x - 2 = 3x + 10$

   (2) $7x + 8.1 = 4x - 2.7$

   (3) $5(8 - y) = 3$

   (4) $4(y + 5) - 13 = -5$

   (5) $2(a - 7) = 2(3 - a) - 36$

   (6) $1.8(x - 1) = 3.1x + 2.1$

   (7) $\frac{3x}{2} = 1 - \frac{x + 1}{4}$

   (8) $\frac{3y + 6}{8} - \frac{5}{6}y + 1 = \frac{5}{6}$

3. 12 sheets of drawing paper remain when each student has 4 pieces. When 2 additional sheets of paper are given to each student, we are 10 sheets short. How many students are there?

Chapter Exercises

A

1.   Solve the following equations:

(1) $6x = 24$

(2) $-\dfrac{2}{3}x = 8$

(3) $x + 21 = 3$

(4) $5x - 3 = 8$

(5) $10 - 4y = -2$

(6) $110 = 40 - 30x$

(7) $4x + 9 = 7x + 3$

(8) $7m + 6 = 3 - 2m$

(9) $5x - 3.7 = 2x + 2.6$

(10) $18t + 25 = -11t - 56 + 2t$

2.   Solve the following equations:

(1) $4(x + 8) - 7 = 5$

(2) $3x - (2 - x) = 0$

(3) $3(a - 5) = 1 - a$

(4) $2(x + 6) - 5(3x + 2) = 2$

(5) $1.1y + 1.4 = 5 - 0.7y$

(6) $2.7 = 0.18(x - 4)$

(7) $\dfrac{1}{2}x + 5 = 2x + \dfrac{1}{2}$

(8) $t = 1 - \dfrac{5 - t}{3}$

3.   There are three consecutive integers, such as 3, 4, 5, whose sum is 195. Find these integers.

4.   A child is presently 12 years old and his father is 44 years old. In how many years will the age of the father be 3 times that of his child?

5.   A store bought a certain number of eggs at 20 yen each. During shipment to the store eight of the eggs were broken. If the rest of the eggs are sold at 23 yen apiece, the store will receive a profit of 2,516 yen. How many eggs did it buy originally?

6.   The number of students at a school has increased 5% over last year and is now 336. How many students were there last year?

B

1. Solve the following equations:

   (1) $5x - 3(2x - 1) = 2x - 3$

   (2) $2(x - 1) = 10 - 2(2x - 3)$

   (3) $0.6(x - 2) - 1.2(3 - 5x) = 0$

   (4) $1.2(2x - 1) - 2.7(x - 2) = 3.6$

   (5) $\dfrac{x}{4} + \dfrac{1}{2} = \dfrac{x}{3} + \dfrac{1}{6}$

   (6) $a - \dfrac{3a - 1}{4} = 2a - 5$

   (7) $\dfrac{a}{3} - \dfrac{6 - 3a}{4} = \dfrac{4 - a}{3}$

   (8) $\dfrac{x - 3}{6} - \dfrac{3x - 1}{4} = 2$

   (9) $\dfrac{3x - 1}{4} - \dfrac{x - 5}{2} = \dfrac{7x - 2}{3}$

   (10) $\dfrac{4 - 3y}{3} + 1 = \dfrac{6 + 7y}{6} - \dfrac{1}{9}$

2. In the following equations, when x takes the value of the numbers in brackets [ ] determine the value of a so that the equation holds.

   (1) $2x + a = x + 4$ [1]

   (2) $3(x + 4) - 4 - 2a = 1$ [-3]

3. A man could arrive on time for an appointment if he drove his car at 40 km/hour; however, since he leaves 15 minutes late, he drives his car at 50 km/hour and arrives 3 minutes early for his appointment. Find the distance between his starting point and his destination.

4. It takes 12 minutes to fill a tank with water using pipe A and 18 minutes using pipe B. First pipe A was opened, and with the tank still filling, pipe A was closed and pipe B was opened. When pipe B had been open for 3 minutes longer than pipe A, the tank was full. How many minutes was pipe A open?

CHAPTER 5

FUNCTIONS AND PROPORTIONS

The picture above shows an MT-135P meteorological observation rocket (length 3.3 m, diameter 13.5 cm, weight 68.5 kg) which the weather bureau launches every week at Sanriku in Iwate Prefecture. After ignition, the fuel continues burning for 11 seconds, and during this time the rocket attains a speed of 1.2 km/second and rises to an altitude of 8 km. But even after this it continues rising and when, in about 110 seconds, it reaches its highest point (about 60 km), the upper part of the rocket separates and the meteorological observation apparatus is released from the middle, attached to a parachute.

All around us, as in the advanced case of the rocket, we can see many instances of increasing and decreasing quantities. In this chapter we will be concerned with changing quantities, so let's examine these situations.

CHANGES AND FUNCTIONS

 ## Variables

A meteorological rocket increases its speed after it is launched and will reach an altitude of 62 km.

If we let the letter h represent the changing altitude in km, then while the rocket is rising h will take a value from 0 to 62.

Letters that take various values, like h, are called **variables**.

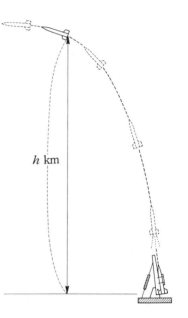

h km

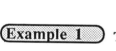 The total weight of the meteorological rocket is 68.5 kg, of which its fuel weighs 37.5 kg. After liftoff, the weight of the rocket will decrease because of fuel consumption.

If we let x represent the weight of the rocket from ignition until the fuel is used up, then x is a variable and the value of x will vary from 31 to 68.5.

To represent the values that the variables can take on we often use the inequality sign. For example, we can show the extent of the values of the variable x if x includes all integers greater than 3 by writing

$$x > 3 \qquad (1)$$

or $\qquad 3 < x.$

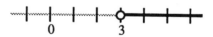

When the scope of the values of x is more than 3 and less than 8, we write

$$3 < x < 8.$$

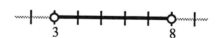

Further, when the extent of the values of x is greater than or equal to 3, we write

$$x \geq 3 \qquad (2)$$

3 is not included among the possible values in (1); it is a possible value in (2).

The extent of all the possible values of a variable is called the **range of the variable.**

The range of the variable h above can be expressed as

$$0 \leq h \leq 62$$

Problem 1   300 m³ of water has been let into a pool which can contain 500 m³ of water. We would like to add enough water to fill up the pool. If we let v m³ represent the total quantity of water in the pool, write an inequality to express the range of the variable v from the present to the time when the pool is full.

Problem 2   If the variable x has the following ranges of values, express these ranges using an inequality sign.

(1)   The range of all positive numbers.

(2)   The range of values greater than or equal to -5 and less than or equal to 5.

   Functions

Corresponding Variable Quantities

On page 97 we examined how the altitude of the rocket increased with time.

If we let h km represent the altitude of the rocket at t seconds after launch, the relation between t and h can be expressed in a graph such as the one at the right. In this instance, t and h are variables, but if t changes then h will also change, and if the value of t is determined, then the value of h is also determined.

For example, when the value of t is 20, the value of h is 18. Here we can say that $t = 20$ corresponds to $h = 18$. We write this as follows:

$$20 \rightarrow 18$$

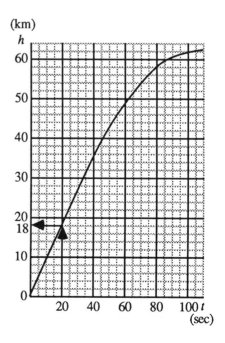

Problem 1   From the graph above
find the values of h
which correspond
to $t = 65$ and
$t = 95$.

t		h
20	→	18
65	→	☐
95	→	☐

The altitude and the time after the rocket has taken off are two corresponding variable quantities. If you determine the value of one, the value of the other is also determined.

There are various examples of this.

Example 1   If we fill an empty water tank
by adding water at a rate of 20
liters every minute, the
quantity of water in the tank
changes with the time taken
to add the water. If in
t minutes v liters are added,
once we determine the value
of t, then the value of v is
also determined.

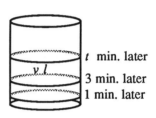

t min. later

v l.

3 min. later

1 min. later

Problem 2   In Example 1, find the values of v corresponding to $t = 3$ and $t = 8$.

Problem 3   If the length of one side of a square has been determined, have you also determined the area? Further, if you determine only the width of a rectangle, have you also determined its area?

Functions

When quantities vary in accordance with changes in other quantities, all these quantities are expressed as variables such as x and y. If we determine the value of x, the value of y is also determined. In situations like this, we say that y **is a function of** x.

In the example of the rocket, h is a function of t.

Let us consider how to express y in terms of x when y is a function of x.

When we open a rectangular window whose height is 50 cm only x cm, we can let y cm^2 represent the area of the open portion. Because determining the value of x allows us also to determine the value of y, y is a function of x.

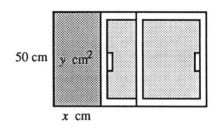

50 cm

x cm

We can express y in terms of x in the following way:

$$y = 50x \qquad (1)$$

That is, the area of a rectangle whose height is 50 cm is a function of its width, and (1) is an expression that shows this function.

Problem 4 Using the function in (1), fill out the chart below by finding the values of y that correspond to the various values of x.

x	5	10	15	20	25	30
y						

The correspondence between the values of x and y in the function in (1) can be expressed by using the following arrow and words.

multiply by 50

$x \longrightarrow y$

Problem 5 For the function in (1), find the range of y when the range of x is $0 \le x \le 30$.

Problem 6 If we let y cm represent the perimeter of a rectangle 4 cm long and x cm wide, y is a function of x. Answer the following questions.

(1) Write y in terms of x.

(2) Find the numbers to fill in the chart below.

x	1	2	3	4	5
y					

(3) Indicate the correspondence between x and y using an arrow and words.

multiply by ( ) and add ( )

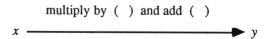

$x \longrightarrow y$

Problem 7 In cases (1)–(3) below, express y in terms of x. Also, find the range of y when the range of x is $1 \leq x \leq 4$.

(1) y km is the distance traveled by a car moving at 40 km/hour for x hours.

(2) y cm^2 is the area of a square whose perimeter is x cm.

(3) y liters is the amount of water remaining in a tank that originally held 100 liters of water after we have removed water at a rate of 10 liters per minute for x minutes.

Problem 8 For the functions in the following expressions, find the value of y that corresponds to $x = 2, x = 0$, and $x = -1$.

(1) $y = 5x - 8$

(2) $y = \dfrac{x + 2}{3}$

Exercises

1. The diagrams below show that when the value of the variable x is defined, a calculation is made in accordance with the rules for each box. Think of the operation occurring in box F and box G, and express the relation between x and y using an arrow and words.

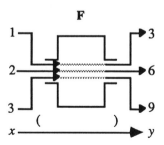
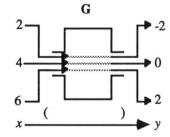

PROPORTIONS AND INVERSE PROPORTIONS

You learned about proportions and inverse proportions in elementary school. Now we will learn about functions which are defined by proportions and inverse proportions.

  Proportions

When we ride an escalator up, we let x m represent the horizontal distance traveled from a point A, and we let y m represent the vertical distance. The relation between x and y can be written as follows:

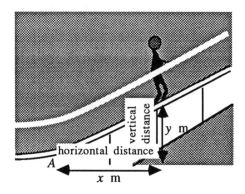

x	0	1	2	3	4	5	6	7	8
y	0	0.6	1.2	1.8	2.4	3.0	3.6	4.2	4.8

Problem 1 Answer the following questions about the chart above.

(1) If the value of x is doubled, tripled, or quadrupled, by what factor must you multiply y to get a corresponding value?

(2) Write the relation between x and y as an expression.

Problem 2 A train whose speed is 1.2 km/minute travels y km in x minutes. Express y in terms of x.

> ### Expressing Proportions
>
> When the following relation exists between two variables x and y, we say that y is **proportional** to x.
>
> $$y = ax$$ a is defined as a fixed number not equal to 0

A fixed number or a symbol that expresses such a number, as in the example above, is called a constant.

The symbol a in the above expression is a constant, and can be called the **constant of proportionality**. The constant of proportionality is equal to the value of y when $x = 1$.

Problem 3   In (1) and (2) below express y in terms of x and show how y is proportional to x. Also point out the constant of proportionality.

(1) y cm^2 is the area of a triangle of base 12 cm and height x cm.

(2) y cm is the circumference of a circle whose radius is x cm.

Example 1 y is proportional to x, and when $x = 6$, $y = 4$. Solve the following problems.

(1)   Express y in terms of x.

(2)   Find the value of y for $x = 9$ and $x = 15$.

[**Solution**]   (1)   If we take a as the constant of proportionality, we can write $y = ax$.

Since when $x = 6$, $y = 4$, if we substitute these values, then

$$4 = a \times 6, \text{ that is, } a = \frac{2}{3}$$

Accordingly,

$$y = \frac{2}{3}x$$

(2)   In the equation we found in (1),

substitute $x = 9$, and $y = \dfrac{2}{3} \times 9 = 6$

substitute $x = 15$, and $y = \dfrac{2}{3} \times 15 = 10$

Answer:
$$\begin{cases} (1) \ y = \dfrac{2}{3}x \\ (2) \ \text{when} \ x = 9, \ y = 6 \\ \qquad \text{when} \ x = 15, y = 10 \end{cases}$$

Problem 4   We would like to cut exactly 160 m of wire. Instead of measuring the length, we measure the weight, and we find that 3 meters of wire weighs 75 grams. Now, solve the following problems.

(1)   If x m of wire weighs y g, express y in terms of x.

(2)   What is the weight of 160 m of wire?

Problem 5   A car travels 12 km on one liter of gasoline. Express y in terms of x if the car uses y liters of gasoline to travel x km. Also, find the range of values of y when the value of x ranges from $60 \le x \le 120$.

Problem 6   On the number line, a point P is moving in a positive direction from the origin O, and a point Q is moving in a negative direction from O.

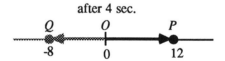

The speeds of both P and Q are constant. Both leave O at the same time, and 4 seconds later P has reached 12 and Q has reached -8. Answer the following questions, letting y be the point reached by P and z be the point reached by Q after x seconds.

(1)   Express both y and z in terms of x.

(2)   30 seconds after leaving point O, how far apart are P and Q?

Inverse Proportions

If we let x cm be the width and y cm be the length of a rectangle whose area is 12 cm², then x and y stand in the relation.

$$xy = 12.$$

When the value of x is changed while the area of this rectangle remains constant, the changes in the value of y are as shown in the chart below.

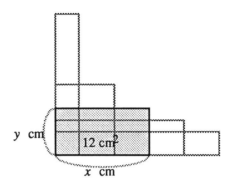

x	...	0.5	1	2	3	4	5	6	...
y	...	24	12	6	4	3	2.4	2	...

In this case, y is a function of x and can be expressed in the following terms:

$$y = \frac{12}{x}$$

Problem 1 Considering x and y above, by what factor will the value of y increase if the value of x doubles, triples, or quadruples?

Expressing Inverse Proportions

When the following relation holds between two variables x and y, y is said to be **inversely proportional** to x.

$$y = \frac{a}{x} \quad \cdots a \text{ is a fixed number not equal to 0.}$$

The number a defined above is a constant of proportionality. When y is inversely proportional to x, the value of xy is fixed and equal to the constant of proportionality.

Problem 2   In (1) and (2) below, express y in terms of x and show that y is inversely proportional to x.

(1) The area of a triangle is 8 cm², its base is x cm, and its height is y cm.

(2) A cogwheel with 20 teeth turns 6 times every minute. It meshes with another cogwheel which has x teeth and makes y revolutions every minute.

Note: Just as you have used x to represent the number of teeth on a cogwheel, the value of a variable may be limited to a natural number.

Problem 3 y is inversely proportional to x, and when $x = 8, y = 12$. Do the following problems.

(1) Substitute $x = 8$ and $y = 12$ into $y = \dfrac{a}{x}$ and determine the value of a. Then express y in terms of x.

(2) Find the value of y for $x = 20$.

Example 1   An empty water tank can be completely filled by adding 3 m³ of water per minute for 80 minutes.

(1) When we add x m³ of water every minute, it takes y minutes to fill up the tank. Express y in terms of x.

(2) If we decide to add 5 m³ of water every minute, how long will it take to fill up the tank?

[Solution]   (1) Since the tank can hold $3 \times 80 = 240$ (m³) of water,

$$xy = 240, \text{ that is, } y = \frac{240}{x}$$

(2) If you substitute $x = 5$, $y = \dfrac{240}{5} = 48$ (minutes)

Answer: (1) $y = \dfrac{240}{x}$

(2) 48 minutes

Problem 4 A certain quantity of fuel will last 30 hours if we use it at a rate of 0.2 liters per hour. If we let x liters represent the amount consumed every hour and y hours the time, express y in terms of x. Further, when the value of x ranges from $0.5 \le x \le 2$, find the range of values of y.

Exercises

1. y is a function of x, and when $x = 2$, $y = -3$. For (1) and (2) below express y in terms of x:

   (1) when y is proportional to x.

   (2) when y is inversely proportional to x.

2. The bottom of a rectangular container is 40 cm long and 20 cm wide. If we let 200 cm^3 of water into the container every second for t seconds, the depth of the water becomes h cm. Answer the following problems:

   (1) Express h in terms of t and show that h is proportional to t.

   (2) Is t proportional to h? If so, state the constant of proportionality.

3. The relation between two variables x and y is given as follows. Express y in terms of x, and find the numbers to fill in the blanks.

   (1) y is proportional to x.

   (2) y is inversely proportional to x.

x	0			9	12
y		9	18	27	

x	1		4		6
y		3	1.5	1.2	

COORDINATES AND GRAPHS

1 Coordinates

You learned in elementary school that the graph of the proportion represented by $y = 2x$ looks like the graph on the right.

Here we will learn how to draw graphs involving negative numbers as well as positive numbers.

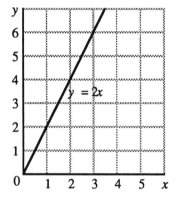

Two number lines are placed as in the diagram at the right, so that one is horizontal and the other vertical, and so that their point of intersection is at O. The horizontal axis is called the **x-axis**, and the vertical axis is called the **y-axis**. The x-axis and the y-axis are referred to as **coordinate axes**, and point O is called the **origin**.

On the x-axis the positive direction is to the right, and on the y-axis the positive direction is upward.

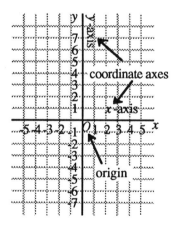

In order to show the position of point P on the graph at the right, we draw perpendiculars from P to the x-axis and to the y-axis, and there we read the marks of points M and N, the intersections with the coordinate axes. Then we pair the mark 3 of M and the mark 4 of N to express the position of point P by (3,4).

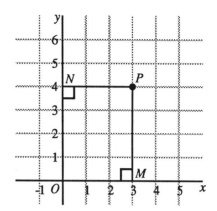

We call (3,4) the **coordinates** of point P: 3 is the **x-coordinate** of P, and 4 is the **y-coordinate** of P. We write point P as $P(3,4)$.

$P(3,4)$ is located 3 units to the right of and 4 units up from the origin.

In this way, any point on a plane can be expressed by a set of two numbers. For any pair of numbers there is only one corresponding point on a plane.

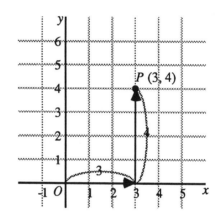

Note: On axes with coordinates, the x- and y-axes usually have the same scale.

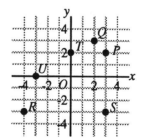**Problem 1** On the graph at the right identify the coordinates of the points $P, Q, R, S, T,$ and U.

Problem 2 Plot the following points on a piece of graph paper:

$A(3,6)$ $B(6,3)$ $C(0,-2)$

$D(0,0)$ $E(4,0)$ $F(-4,0.5)$

Problem 3 For each of the following points, find the coordinates of the points that are symmetric to them with respect to the x-axis. Find the points symmetric to them with respect to the y-axis and to the origin.

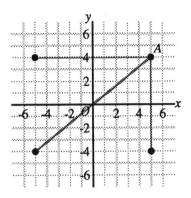

A(5,4)

B(6,-2)

C(-2,-3)

Problem 4 Find the coordinates of the original points in Problem 3 if they are moved:

(1)   3 units to the right   (2)   2 units up

Problem 5 A plane can be divided by the coordinate axes into four parts, I, II, III, and IV, as shown to the right, provided that the points of the axes themselves are excluded.

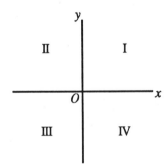

The x and y coordinates of the points in part I are both positive. Examine the signs of the x and y coordinates of the points in the other parts.

part	I	II	III	IV
sign of x-coordinate	+			
sign of y-coordinate	+			

Graphing Functions

The Graph of $y = ax$

When y is proportional to x and when

$$y = 2x \qquad\qquad (1)$$

we can chart the values of y that correspond to the various values of x in the following way.

x	...	-4	-3	-2	-1	0	1	2	3	4	...
y	...	-8	-6	-4	-2	0	2	4	6	8	...

If we plot the points whose coordinates are the paired values of x and y in the above chart, we get the figure shown at the right.

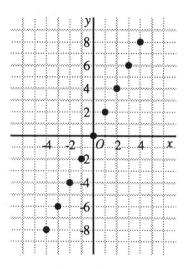

Problem 1 In function (1), take values of x at intervals of 0.5 from -4 to 4, and find the value of y that corresponds to each value of x. Then make a chart and plot the points on the figure at the right.

If we plot all the points whose coordinates are the paired values of x and y for the function $y = 2x$, they form a single straight line.

We refer to the straight line obtained in this way as the **graph of the function** $y = 2x$.

This straight line is an extended example of the graph on page 108.

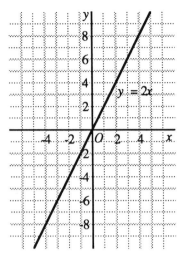

Problem 2 Graph the following functions:

(1) $y = 3x$

(2) $y = -2x$

(3) $y = \frac{1}{2}x$

(4) $y = -\frac{1}{2}x$

Problem 3 For $y = 2x$, when x increases, does y increase too, or decrease? What happens in the case of $y = -2x$?

The Graph of $y = ax$

When a is a constant, the graph of $y = ax$ is a straight line that passes through the origin.

(1) For $a > 0$, the graph is a straight line that slopes upward from left to right, and when x increases, y increases as well.

(2) For $a < 0$, the graph is a straight line that slopes downward from left to right, and when x increases, y decreases.

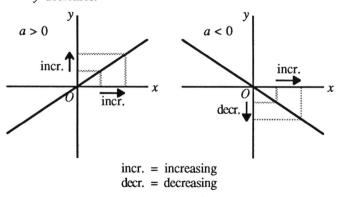

incr. = increasing
decr. = decreasing

Problem 4 Graph the function $y = 2x$, and find how much y increases each time x increases by 1.

Problem 5 Graph the function $y = \frac{2}{3}x$, when the value of x ranges from $-3 \le x \le 3$. Also find the range of values of y.

Problem 6 The water level at a dam is rising at a constant rate. If we take the water level at a certain time as the standard, the graph below indicates changes in the water level. We will let y cm represent the change in the water level x hours after the standard level has been reached.

(1) How many centimeters has the water level risen 4 hours after the standard time? Also, what is the water level 2 hours before the standard time?

(2) How much does the water level rise every hour?

(3) Express y in terms of x.

The Graph of $y = \dfrac{a}{x}$

Let us graph $y = \dfrac{12}{x}$.

If we make a chart of the values of y corresponding to the values of x, it will look like this:

x		...	-12	-6	-4	-3	-2	-1	1	2	3	4	6	12	...
y		...	-1	-2	-3	-4	-6	-12	12	6	4	3	2	1	...

Note: Since it is impossible to divide by 0, there is no value of y that corresponds to $x = 0$.

Problem 7 Plot all the points whose coordinates are the paired values of x and y from the chart above. Also find the values of y that correspond to $x = 0.5$ and $x = 24$.

If we plot additional points whose coordinates are the paired values of x and y for the function $y = \dfrac{12}{x}$, the totality of all such points will be the curve shown below. This curve is the graph of $y = \dfrac{12}{x}$

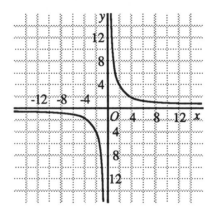

Problem 8 Graph the following functions:

(1) $y = \dfrac{6}{x}$
(2) $y = -\dfrac{12}{x}$

Generally, when a is a nonzero constant, the graph of $y = \dfrac{a}{x}$ consists of two smooth curves. This curve is called a hyperbola.

Problem 9 In the graph of $y = \dfrac{12}{x}$, compare the points that correspond to $x = 1$ and $x = -1$ and the points that correspond to $x = 2$ and $x = -2$, and then check that the graph is symmetric with respect to the origin. Do the same for the graph of $y = -\dfrac{12}{x}$.

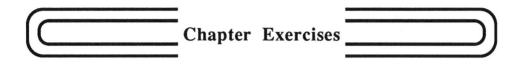

Chapter Exercises

A

1. When we read a 240-page book, we can let x represent the number of pages we have read and y represent the number of pages that remain to be read. Given this context, answer the following problems:

    (1) Express y in terms of x.

    (2) How many pages have we read when y is exactly twice x?

2. Express y in terms of x for the following relations. State whether y is directly proportional or inversely proportional to x.

    (1) When we add x g of water to a cup that weighs 30 g, the total weight is y g.

    (2) If one liter of paint costs x yen, then y liters is the amount of paint we can buy for 1,000 yen.

    (3) By bending a 20 cm length of wire we can make a rectangle. When the length of this rectangle is y cm, the width is x cm.

    (4) A rocket moving at a speed of 1.2 km/second travels a distance of y km in x seconds.

3. Find the area of the triangle in which the following three points are vertices, given that one unit equals 1 cm.

    (1) $A(1,4)$ $B(5, 1)$ $C(4, 7)$

    (2) $E(5, -1)$, $F(2, 4)$ $G(-3, -2)$

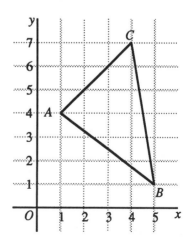

4. Below are graphs of proportions and inverse proportions. Find the constant of proportionality for each graph, and express each y in terms of x.

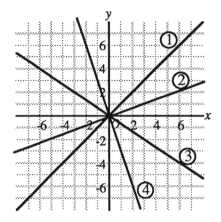 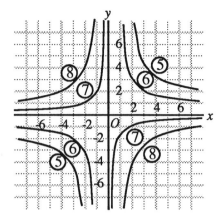

B

1. We have balanced a lever, as shown in the diagram to the right, by hanging weights on either side of the fulcrum O. If we let the distances from O equal a cm and b cm and the two weights equal x g and y g, respectively, then the relation among $a, b, x,$ and y is

   $$ax = by$$

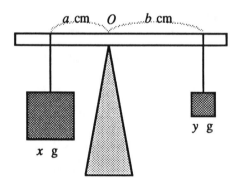

Given this information, answer the following questions.

(1) When $a = 8$ and $b = 10$, is y directly proportional or inversely proportional to x?

(2) When $a = 8$ and $x = 100$, is y directly proportional or inversely proportional to b?

2. 4 m of wire weighs 160 g, and 100 g of this wire costs 120 yen. If the cost of x m of this wire is y yen, write an expression showing the relation between x and y.

CHAPTER 6

PLANE FIGURES

The family of Mr. A raises cows. Every morning, Mr. A goes to the cow shed carrying buckets of feed, and on his way back he goes down to the stream, washes the buckets, and returns to the house. Looking for different places to wash the buckets, he noticed that the distance he walked to get to those places varied. Then he decided he would like to keep the distance he had to walk as short as possible, so he used the diagram below to figure out where on the river he should wash the buckets.

How was he able to decide which was the shortest distance to walk?

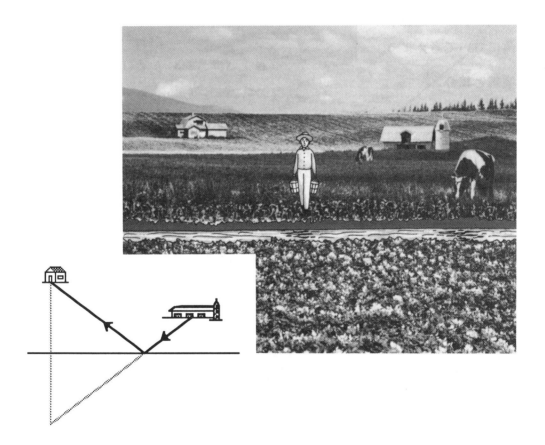

STRAIGHT LINES AND CIRCLES

Straight Lines and Angles

We see various shapes every day, and in this section we will study simple figures: straight lines and angles.

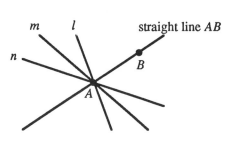

Straight Lines and Line Segments

Usually when we speak about a straight line, we think of it as something that extends infinitely in both directions.

You can draw any number of lines that pass through a single point *A*, like line *m* and line *n* in the diagram to the right. However, there is only one straight line that passes through both points *A* and *B*. We refer to the line that passes through points *A* and *B* as **straight line *AB***.

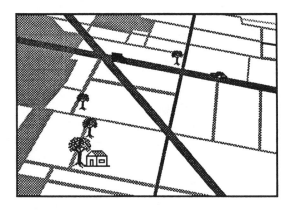

The part of line *AB* which connects point *A* and point *B* is called a line segment, **segment *AB***.

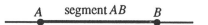

Problem 1 In the diagram to the right, which is the shortest line that connects points *A* and *B*?

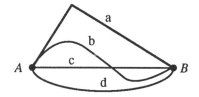

The length of a segment AB is the distance between points A and B.

A point O on a line divides the line into two parts. Each part is called a **ray**.

Angles

We can make an angle by drawing two rays OA and OB from a point O. The point O is called the vertex of the angle, and the two rays OA and OB are called the sides of the angle.

The angle shown in the diagram is designated by the symbol $\angle AOB$ and is read "angle AOB." When there is no possibility of confusion, it can be written using only the vertex, as in $\angle O$, or by using a lower case letter to identify the angle, as in $\angle a$.

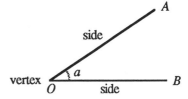

Problem 2 In the diagram to the right the angles are shown as $\angle x$, $\angle y$, and $\angle z$. Designate them using the letters $A, B, C,$ and D.

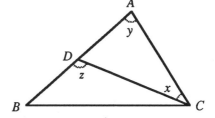

Circles and Sectors

Circles

Circles can be drawn by using a compass. After drawing a circle in this way, you can see that the circumference of a circle is the figure obtained when a point in a plane moves at a fixed distance from a second point (the center).

A circle whose center is at O is referred to as **circle** O.

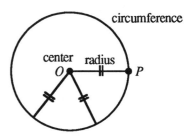

> **Note:** The circumference of a circle can be termed simply the circle.

In the figure to the right, radius OA equals half the length of diameter AB. This is written in the following way:

$$OA = \frac{1}{2}AB \quad \text{or,} \quad AB = 2OA.$$

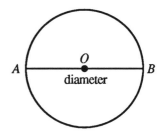

Arcs and Chords

If we mark two points A and B on a circle, the portion of the circle from A to B is called an **arc.** The arc with endpoints A and B is referred to as arc AB, and is designated by $\overset{\frown}{AB}$.

The segment that connects the endpoints is called a **chord.** A chord whose endpoints are A and B is referred to as chord AB.

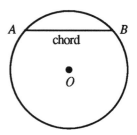

Problem 1   In the figure to the right, if we fix the position of point P and move point Q along the circumference of circle O in the direction of the arrow, when will the length of chord PQ be the greatest?

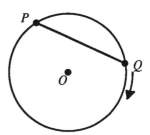

Sectors

A sector is a figure composed of an arc and the two radii that pass through the endpoints of that arc. The angle made by the two radii is called the central angle subtended by the arc, or the central angle of the sector.

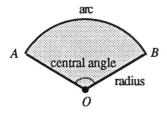
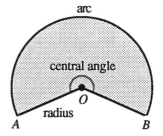

Problem 2   Draw a circle of radius 4 cm, and construct a sector OAB whose central angle is 60°.

In the same circle, two sectors with equal central angles can be rotated around the center so that one sector overlaps the other sector. Accordingly, both the lengths of the arcs and the areas of two sectors with equal central angles in the same circle are equal.

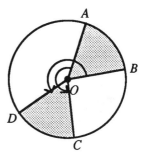

Problem 3 In the figure to the right, if we double and triple the central angle of sector *OAB* and construct sectors *OBC* and *OCD*, how long are $\overset{\frown}{BC}$ and $\overset{\frown}{CD}$ compared to $\overset{\frown}{AB}$? Also, how much larger are the areas of sectors *OBC* and *OCD* than the area of sector *OAB*?

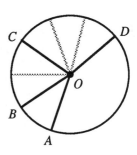

The Arcs and Areas of Sectors

In the same circle, the lengths of the arcs and the areas of the sectors are proportional to the central angles.

π and Its Approximate Value

The ratio of the circumference to the diameter is the same for all circles. This ratio is called *pi* and is usually written with the Greek letter π.

π is the infinitely continuing number 3.141592..., but as a roughly equivalent value either 3.14 or 3.1416 can be used.

Such kinds of roughly equivalent values as 3.14 or 3.1416 are called **approximate values.** Values obtained by rounding off, as well as values obtained by practical measurement, are approximate values.

Circumferences and the Lengths of Arcs

We will recall that

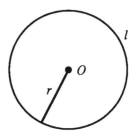

(length of circumference)   = (diameter) $\times$ π

= (radius) $\times$ 2 $\times$ π

If we let the radius of a circle be r, then we can express the circumference of circle l by the formula

$$l = 2\pi r$$

Example 1   The circumference of a circle whose radius is 7 cm is

$$2\pi r = 2 \times \pi \times 7$$

$$= 14\pi$$

Therefore, the circumference of the circle is 14π cm.

Problem 4   Express the circumference of a circle whose radius is 5 cm using π.

In a circle of radius r, the length l of an arc whose central angle is $a°$ can be found in the following way.

$$l = 2\pi r \times \frac{a}{360}$$

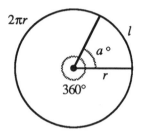

Example 2   The length of the arc of a sector with radius 5 cm and central angle 30° is

$$2 \times \pi \times 5 \times \frac{30}{360} = \frac{5\pi}{6}$$

Thus, the length of the arc is $\frac{5\pi}{6}$ cm.

In Example 2, if we take 3.14 as the approximate value of π, the length of the arc is 2.616666... cm, but we may round this figure off to 2.62 cm. In general, in calculations with approximate values there is no sense in writing more digits than necessary.

Problem 5   Using π, find the length of an arc with a radius of 6 cm and a central angle of 45°.

Problem 6   With π as 3.14, find the central angle of a sector whose radius is 10 cm and whose arc is 15.7 cm long.

Note: From now on, unless problems specify otherwise, we will use π to calculate instead of approximate values.

Area of Circles and Sectors

Because

$$(\text{area of a circle}) = (\text{radius})^2 \times \pi,$$

if we let r be the radius of circle S, the area can be expressed by the formula

$$S = \pi r^2$$

(**Problem 7**) Find the area of a circle whose radius is 5 cm.

In a circle of radius r, the area S of a sector whose central angle is $a°$ can be found in the following way.

$$S = \pi r^2 \times \frac{a}{360}$$

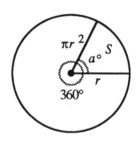

(**Problem 8**) Find the area of a sector whose radius is 6 cm and whose central angle is 60°.

(**Problem 9**) Find the area and the circumference of a semicircle whose diameter is 8 cm.

(**Problem 10**) Letting S be the area of a sector whose radius is r and whose arc length is l, solve the following problems.

(1) Write an expression to find both l and S when the central angle is $a°$.

(2) Show that the following relation holds among s, l, and r:

$$S = \frac{1}{2} lr$$

Exercises

1. The following figures combine sectors and squares. Find the perimeter and area of the shaded portions.

(1)

(2)

(3)

(4)

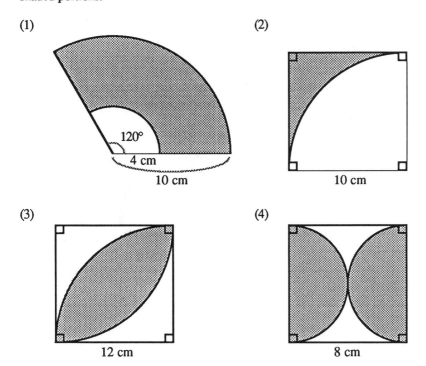

CONSTRUCTING FIGURES AND SETS OF POINTS

  Basic Constructions

Problem 1   Using a compass and a ruler, construct a figure like the one to the right.

Until now, we have not specified the use of tools when constructing figures, but in this chapter we will use compasses and rulers to construct our figures. Compasses are used to construct circles, and rulers are used to draw straight lines.

Angle Bisectors and Their Construction

A ray that divides an angle into two equal angles is said to be the **bisector** of that angle.

If we let ray *OM* be a bisector of ∠*AOB*, then

$$\angle AOM = \angle BOM = \frac{1}{2} \angle AOB$$

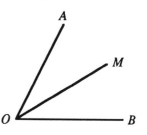

Using a compass and ruler, let us construct the bisector of an angle.

(1) Taking as its center point *O*, the vertex of ∠*AOB*, construct a circle with a fairly long radius, and let *C* and *D* be the points of intersection with the two sides *OA* and *OB* of the angle.

(2) Construct two circles of equal radii with *C* and *D* as their centers, and let the point of intersection be *E*, as in the figure to the right.

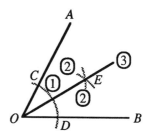

(3) Draw the ray *OE*.

OE is the bisector of ∠*AOB*.

Problem 2 Construct ∠*AOB* on tracing paper, and construct the angle bisector *OE* as above. Next, fold the paper so that *OA* lies upon *OB*, and see whether *OE* disappears in the fold.

Problem 3 Draw any kind of triangle, and construct angle bisectors for each of the three angles.

Perpendiculars and Their Construction

Problem 4 Given that ∠*AOB* = 180°, construct the angle bisector *OC* of ∠*AOB*.

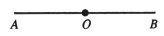

If *OC* is the angle bisector of ∠*AOB*

and ∠*AOB* = 180°

then

∠*AOC* = ∠*BOC* = 90°.

When the angle formed by two intersecting straight lines is a right angle, we say that these two lines are perpendicular, and that one line is the **perpendicular** to the other.

We denote the fact that two lines *AB* and *CD* are perpendicular by writing

$$AB \perp CD$$

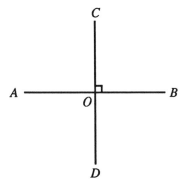

The Perpendicular Bisector of a Segment and Its Construction

The point that bisects a segment is called the **midpoint** of that segment. Also, the perpendicular straight line that passes through the midpoint of a segment is called the **perpendicular bisector** of that segment.

We can construct the perpendicular bisector of segment AB as follows.

(1) Construct two circles of equal radii with centers at A and B, and let C and D be the points of intersection.

(2) Draw line CD.

CD is the perpendicular bisector of segment AB.

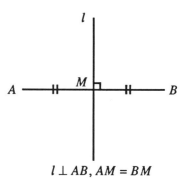

$l \perp AB, AM = BM$

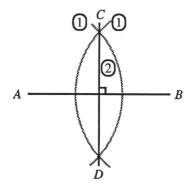

 Problem 5 Draw a segment AB on tracing paper, and construct line CD as above. Next, fold the paper so that point A lies on point B, and see whether line CD is hidden by the fold. From this, consider why $CD \perp AB$.

If we let M be the point of intersection of AB and CD in the drawing you have made, then M is the midpoint of segment AB. By constructing the perpendicular bisector of a segment in this way we can find the midpoint of that segment.

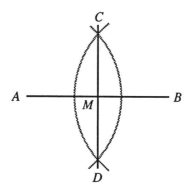

 Problem 6 Draw any triangle and construct the perpendicular bisectors of each of the three sides.

Constructing a Perpendicular to a Line from a Point That Is Not on the Line

From a point P which is not on line l, we can draw a line perpendicular to line l as follows.

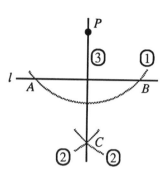

(1) Draw a circle with a radius of convenient length and its center at P, and let A and B be the points of intersection with l.

(2) Construct circles of equal radii with centers A and B. Call one of the two points of intersection C.

(3) Draw line PC.

Line PC is perpendicular to l.

Problem 7 Using the same method, draw a line from point A perpendicular to line l in the figure to the right.

• A

l ─────────────

Problem 8 To draw a line perpendicular to l and passing through point P not on line l, you can also apply the method in the figure to the right, utilizing two circles whose centers are any two points on line l. Describe how to construct a perpendicular line in this way.

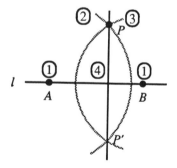

Distances between Points and Lines

If Q is the point of intersection of line AB and a line perpendicular to AB and passing through point P, the length of segment PQ is said to be the **distance** between point P and line AB. PQ is the shortest segment connecting point P to a point on line AB.

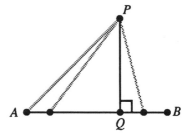

Note:

Usually, when we speak of distance, we mean the shortest length.

Problem 9

Among the points $A - F$ on the graph paper at the right, which point is the nearest to line l? Which is the farthest from line l?

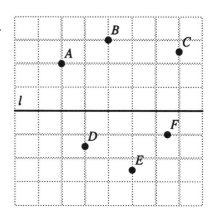

② Figures and Sets of Points

Problem 1

Pick a point O and plot several points at a distance of 3 cm from O. What kind of figure does the set of all those points make?

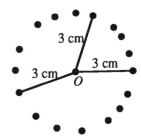

On a plane, the set of all the points at a fixed distance r from a fixed point O is the circumference of a circle of radius r which has its center at O.

Problem 2 Pick any point P above the bisector of $\angle AOB$, and compare the distance from point P to each side of the angle.

Problem 3 In the figure at the right, OC is the bisector of $\angle AOB$. Taking any point P inside $\angle AOC$, compare the distance from P to the two sides of $\angle AOB$. What would be the result if we took point P to be inside $\angle BOC$?

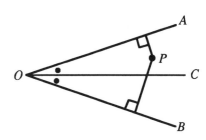

Inside an angle, the angle bisector is the set of all the points for which the distance to each side of the angle is equal.

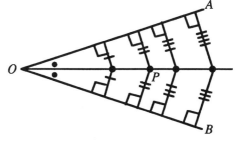

Problem 4 In the figure to the right, we have a circle O and two lines l and m that intersect the circle. Find the points on circle O for which the distance to l and m is equal.

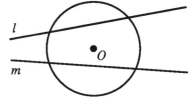

Problem 5 In the figure to the right, two segments AC and BD extend from the ends of segment AB. We would like to find a point O which is at the same distance from AB, AC, and BD. How would we go about it?

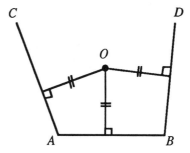

Problem 6   Take a point *P* on the perpendicular bisector of segment *AB*, and draw lines from *P* to *A*, and from *P* to *B*, and then compare the lengths of *PA* and *PB*.

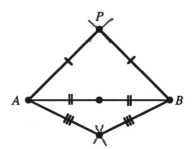

Problem 7   Establish two points *A* and *B* and plot many points equidistant from *A* and *B*, as illustrated by point *P* to the right. What kind of figure will be formed by the set of these points?

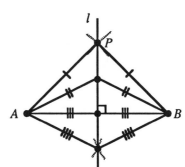

On a plane, the set of all points equidistant from two fixed points is the perpendicular bisector of the segment which connects those two points.

Problem 8   Various circles pass through two fixed points *A* and *B*. What kind of figure will be formed by the set of the centers of all those circles?

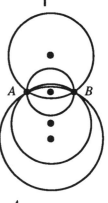

Problem 9   In the diagram at the right, we are given two points *A* and *B* and one line *l*. By construction, find the point on *l* that is equidistant from *A* and *B*.

A •

• *B*

l ————————

Exercises

1. Draw a triangle like the one to the right, and from each of the three vertices draw a perpendicular line to each opposite side.

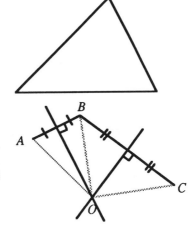

2. Point O in the figure to the right is the point at which the perpendicular bisector of segment BC intersects the perpendicular bisector of segment AB. What is the relation among the lengths of segments OA, OB, and OC?

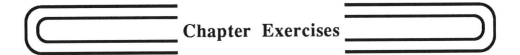

Chapter Exercises

A

1. Four points $A, B, C,$ and D are arranged in order on one straight line such that

$$AB = BC = CD.$$

Indicate the relation between the lengths of AC and BD by means of an expression. Also, indicate the relation between AC and CD by means of an expression.

2. In the figure to the right there are two circles with radii of 4 cm and 6 cm, respectively. Find the circumference and the area of the shaded portion.

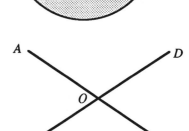

6 cm

4 cm

3. Find the area of a sector with radius 5 cm and central angle 60° and the area of a sector with radius 10 cm and central angle 60°, and compare the two areas.

4. In the figure to the right, two lines AB and CD intersect at point O. Construct angle bisectors OE and OF for $\angle AOD$ and $\angle BOD$.

5. In the previous problem, if $\angle AOD = 120°$, what will be the measure of $\angle EOF$?

6. If we are given two points A and B 5 cm apart, how many points will satisfy both conditions (a) and (b)? Do any points satisfy both (a) and (c)?

   (a) The distance from A is 3 cm.

   (b) The distance from B is 4 cm.

   (c) The distance from B is 1 cm.

B

1. Three points A, B, and C are arranged in order on one line such that

$$AB = 2BC.$$

Let M be the midpoint of AB and N be the midpoint of BC. If $MN = 15$ cm, how long is AB?

2. The following figures are combinations of sectors and rectangles. Find the perimeter and area of the shaded portions.

①

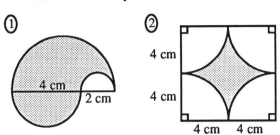

②

③

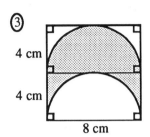

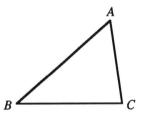

3. Draw a triangle ABC like the one to the right, and find the points for (1) and (2) below by construction.

    (1) The intersection point D of side BC and the angle bisector of $\angle BAC$.

    (2) The intersection point E of a perpendicular line drawn from D to side AB and AB.

4. In the figure to the right,

$$\angle AOD = \angle COB = 90°$$

What is the relation between the measures of $\angle AOC$ and $\angle BOD$?

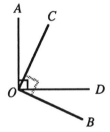

Tracing the Roots of Mathematics

Finding the Circular Constant π

The circumference of a circle is longer than the perimeter of a polygon drawn within the circle and shorter than the perimeter of a polygon which contains the circle in its interior. Archimedes of Greece (3rd century B.C.) devised a 96-sided polygon and discovered that the value of π is greater than $3\frac{10}{71}$ and less than $3\frac{1}{7}$. Tsu Chung-Chih of China (5th century A.D.) found an approximate value for π of $\frac{355}{113}$, and this value was correct to six decimal places – a degree of accuracy not achieved in Europe until the 16th century. During the first part of the 17th century, the Dutchman Rudolf found the value of π to the 35th decimal place, after devoting nearly his entire life to the calculation. In Japan, too, Seki Takakazu (17th century) calculated π using a regular 131,072-gon, but could not extend this to ten decimal places.

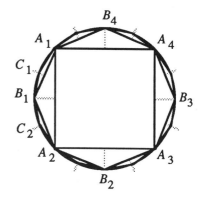

At that point mathematicians stopped basing their calculations on polygons and started thinking about other methods based on numerical expressions, so that at the beginning of the 18th century they were able to find the value of π to 100 decimal places. In 1873, the Englishman Shanks calculated π to 707 decimal places, but in 1946 it was found that he had made a mistake at the 528th decimal place. In 1949, an electronic calculating machine was used for the first time, and π was calculated to 2,035 decimal places. At present, the value of π has been calculated to beyond 1,000,000 decimal places.

Archimedes

$\pi = 3.14159\ 26535\ 89793\ 23846\ 26433\ 83279\ 50288\ 41971\ 69399\ 37510...$

CHAPTER 7

FIGURES IN SPACE

In our everyday life we must make effective use of space. In large train stations with a great number of tracks, platforms are built above as well as below ground in order to avoid confusion and excessive congestion. Through the use of overpasses, cars and trucks can move smoothly along expressways even though there are no traffic lights.

All around us we can see various devices that help us utilize space.

FIGURES IN SPACE

 ## Relations between Straight Lines and Planes

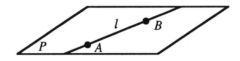

We usually conceive of planes as extending infinitely. Straight line l, passing through two points A and B lying in plane P, is included in plane P. We say that line l lies in plane P.

Straight Lines Parallel to Planes

Two straight lines that are in the same plane and never intersect are called **parallel.** We designate the fact that two straight lines AB and CD are parallel by

$$AB \parallel CD$$

As shown in the figure to the right, if we slide a triangle along the straight line l in a plane, the positions of point P form a straight line m parallel to line l.

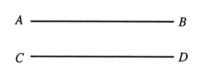

The length of PQ is unchanged. Thus, line m can be thought of as the set of all the points in a plane that are located on one side of line l and at a fixed distance from it. We call this constant distance the distance between parallel lines.

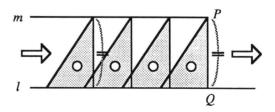

As in the case of a straight line, two planes in space that never intersect are called parallel planes. And when a straight line and a plane never intersect, we say that the line and the plane are parallel.

Problem 1 State which surface is parallel to plane *ABCD* in the rectangular parallelepiped at the right. State which edges are parallel to plane *ABCD*.

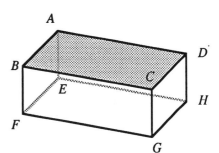

The place at which two planes intersect is a straight line. We call this line the line of intersection of the two planes.

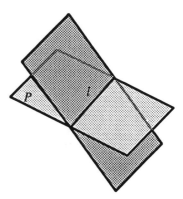

In the triangular prism at the right, *AD* and *CF* are both parallel to *BE*. In such a case, *AD* and *CF* are also parallel. Thus, two lines that are parallel to the same line are also parallel to each other.

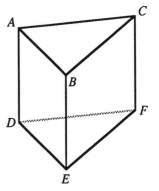

Problem 2 With regard to the rectangular parallelepiped shown in Problem 1, which edges are parallel to *AE*?

Skew Lines

Two lines that are not parallel and do not intersect are called **skew lines**.

In the rectangular parallelepiped to the right *AC* and *FH* are skew lines.

(Problem 3) In the figure to the right, state the relative position of the two lines in each of the following pairs.

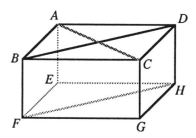

(1) *BD* and *FH*

(2) *BC* and *EH*

(3) *AB* and *FH*

The relative positions of two lines in space can be classified in the following way:

Intersecting at one point......... ⎫
                                    ⎬ ....In the same plane
                         Parallel ⎭
Non-intersecting...⎰
                   ⎱ Skew ....Not in the same plane

Determining Planes

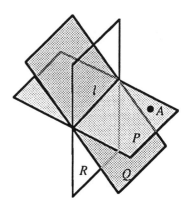

There are any number of planes that contain line *l*, such as *P*, *Q* and *R*, as shown at the right. However, only one plane contains both point *A*, which is not on line *l*, and line *l*. That is, a line and a point not on that line determine only one plane.

Generally, if we have any one of the following conditions, exactly one plane is determined.

(1) One line and a point not on that line.

(2) Two lines that intersect.

(3) Three points which are not on the same line.

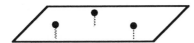

(4) Two parallel lines.

Perpendicular Lines and Planes

Let line l intersect plane P at point O. If line l is perpendicular to every line in P which passes through O, we say that line l is perpendicular to plane P.

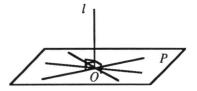

Problem 4 Using two triangles, explain how we can stand a thin rod so that the rod is perpendicular to a plane.

If a line which intersects a plane is perpendicular to two lines that pass through the intersection in the plane, it is perpendicular to the plane.

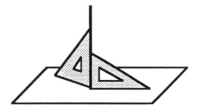

Problem 5 In the rectangular parallelepiped to the right, explain how you know that AE is perpendicular to plane $EFGH$.

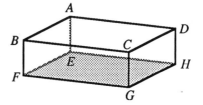

As in the case of points and lines, when H is the point of intersection of plane P and a perpendicular line drawn from a point A to plane P, we say that the length of segment AH is the distance between point A and plane P.

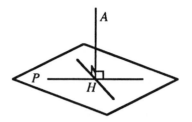

In the diagram below, when we open the cover of a book, the angle between the plane P of the cover and the plane Q of the book gradually increases. The angle between the two planes P and Q is the angle $\angle MON$ formed by two lines, one in each plane, drawn perpendicular to the line of intersection AB of the two planes. When this angle is a right angle, the two planes P and Q are said to be perpendicular.

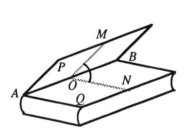

Problem 6   In the rectangular parallelepiped at the right, plane $ABCD$ and plane $AEFB$ are perpendicular. What other surfaces are perpendicular to plane $ABCD$?

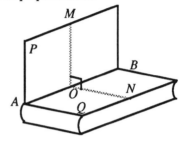

The door shown in the figure at the right is capable of rotating on its axis, line AB, which is perpendicular to the surface P of the floor. This door is always perpendicular to the floor.

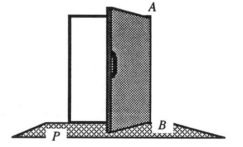

A plane that contains a line which perpendicularly intersects another plane is itself perpendicular to that other plane.

Problem 7 The figure to the right shows a cardboard rectangle *ABCD*, bent along line *EF*, which is parallel to side *AB*, and placed in an upright position on plane *P*. Both the line of the fold *EF* and the plane *ABFE* are perpendicular to plane *P*. Explain how you know this.

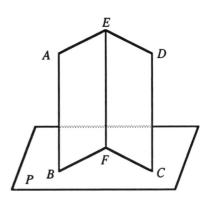

Two Parallel Planes and Their Perpendiculars

In the rectangular parallelepiped below, plane *ABCD* and plane *EFGH* are both perpendicular to one line *BF*, and thus the two planes are parallel.

In general,

(1)   Two planes that are both perpendicular to one line are parallel.

(2)   A line that is perpendicular to either of two parallel planes is also perpendicular to the other plane.

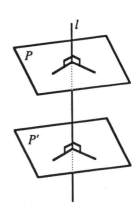

When we draw a line perpendicular to two parallel planes, the length of the line between the two planes does not change, regardless of where you draw the perpendicular. This length equals the distance between the two parallel planes.

In the rectangular parallelepiped to the right, the lengths of segments *AE*, *BF*, *CG*, and *DH* are all the same, and each is the distance between plane *ABCD* and plane *EFGH*.

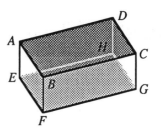

Problem 8   Can we say that each of the following pairs of planes and lines are parallel? Consider each case using the rectangular parallelepiped above.

(1)   Two lines parallel to one plane.
(2)   Two lines perpendicular to one plane.
(3)   Two planes parallel to one line.
(4)   Two lines perpendicular to one line.
(5)   Two planes perpendicular to one plane.

 Polyhedrons

Problem 1   Match the geometric solids (1)–(6) with the corresponding conditions (a)–(c).

(1)   cube   (2)   cylinder   (3)   triangular prism

(4)   sphere   (5)   cone   (6)   rectangular parallelepiped

(a)   bounded only by planes

(b)   bounded only by curved surfaces

(c)   bounded by both planes and curved surfaces

As in the case of a rectangular parallelepiped or a triangular prism, a geometric solid that is bounded only by planes is called a **polyhedron**. Polyhedrons are named according to the number of faces they have, for example, pentahedron or hexahedron. Both a cube and a rectangular parallelepiped have six faces, and so both are hexahedrons.

Problem 2   What kind of polyhedron is a triangular prism?

Pyramids

The polyhedrons shown in the figure at the right are pyramids. They have a triangle *BCD* or a quadrilateral *BCDE* as the base, and have triangular faces, one side of which is shared with the base. The vertex *A* is the point where the lateral faces meet.

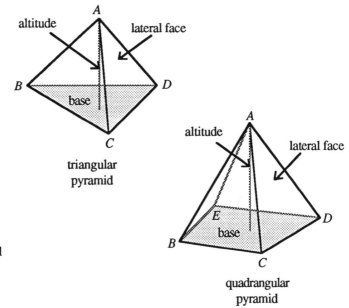

If the base is a pentagon, a hexagon, etc., then we call the polyhedron a pentagonal pyramid, a hexagonal pyramid, etc. The distance between the base of a pyramid and the vertex opposite the base is the altitude of the pyramid.

Some pyramids have bases which are equilateral triangles, squares, etc., and the lengths of the edges that extend from the vertex are all equal; these are called regular triangular pyramids, regular square pyramids, etc. The lateral faces of these regular pyramids are congruent isosceles triangles.

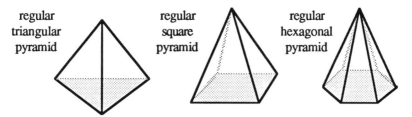

Problem 3 What kinds of polyhedrons are a triangular pyramid and a pentagonal pyramid?

Regular Polyhedrons

The six faces of a cube are all congruent squares, and at each of its vertices three faces intersect.

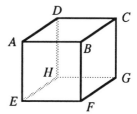

As in the case of the cube, some polyhedrons have the following two properties.

(1)   Every face is congruent.

(2)   Every vertex has the same number of adjoining faces.

Among these polyhedrons those with no indentations are called **regular polyhedrons**. There are five kinds of regular polyhedrons:

> regular tetrahedron   regular dodecahedron,
> regular hexahedron,   regular icosahedron
> regular octahedron,

These are shown below. A cube is a regular hexahedron.

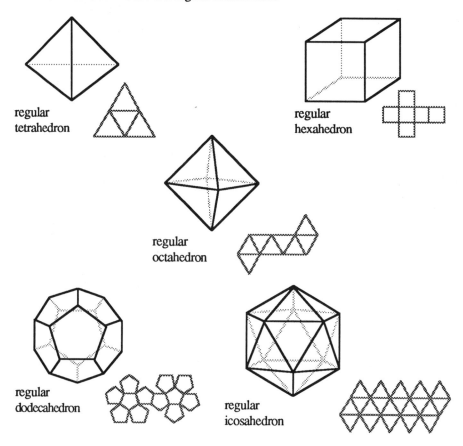

regular
tetrahedron

regular
hexahedron

regular
octahedron

regular
dodecahedron

regular
icosahedron

Problem 4   The figure at the left is a cube formed by connecting the points in the middle of the faces of a regular octahedron. What type of geometric solid will be formed if we do the same thing in a cube? Figure this out using the figure at the right.

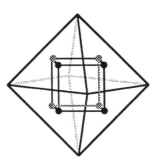

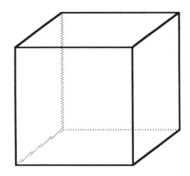

 Forming Geometric Solids from Plane Figures

Triangular prisms, quadrilateral prisms, and so on, can be thought of as geometric solids formed by movement of the base in a perpendicular direction. If a polygon such as a triangle or a quadrilateral is moved perpendicular to its plane, a prism will be formed. If a circle is moved perpendicular to its plane, a cylinder will be formed.

Problem 1   When we move a polygon or a circle as described above, the outline of the polygon or the circumference of the circle will form a surface. What part of a prism or cylinder is this surface?

When the two bases of a prism or cylinder are parallel, the distance between the bases is equal to the altitude of the prism or cylinder.

Solids of Revolution

A cylinder can be thought of as a geometric solid formed by revolving a rectangle about an axis formed by one of its sides. The figure at the right shows a cylinder formed by revolving the rectangle *ABCD* about *CD* as an axis. In this example, side AB forms the lateral face of the cylinder. We call *AB* the **generatrix** of the cylinder.

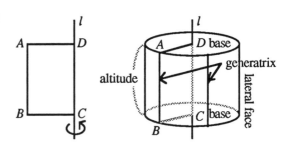

The figures at the right show that a cone is formed by revolving right triangle *ABC* about *AC* as an axis. Side *AB* forms the lateral face of the cone. *AB* is called the generatrix of the cone.

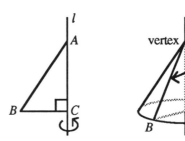

Problem 2 If we cut a cylinder or a cone with a plane that includes the axis of revolution, what shape would the section have? Also, if we cut a circle or a cone with a plane perpendicular to the axis of revolution, what shape would the section have?

Like cylinders and cones, a geometric solid that is formed when a plane figure is revolved about an axis consisting of one line is called a **solid of revolution**.

A sphere is a solid of revolution formed when a semicircle revolves about its diameter as an axis.

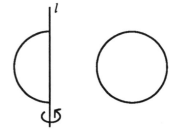

If we cut a solid of revolution with a plane that contains the axis of revolution, the section will be symmetrical with respect to the axis of revolution.

Problem 3 When we cut a sphere with a plane, how can we cut it to obtain the largest possible section?

Problem 4 In the figure to the right, if we revolve quadrilateral *ABCD*, in which ∠*C* and ∠*D* are both right angles, about side *CD* as an axis, what kind of geometric solid will be formed? Make a sketch of this solid.

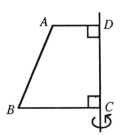

 ## How to Look at and Draw Geometric Solids

When we look at a geometric solid, the shape we can see often changes depending on the direction from which we look. The figures below depict a cube as seen from various viewpoints.

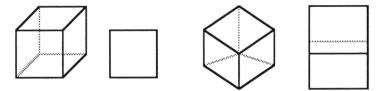

Problem 1 What geometric solid will look the same no matter where you view it from?

You learned how to make a drafting sketch in elementary school; this is one method of representing geometric solids in a plane.

Problem 2 Sketch a triangular prism and a cylinder.

Problem 3 The drawing at the right shows a geometric solid. Taking the shaded area as the front, draw the figures you would see from the front, from the top, and from the left.

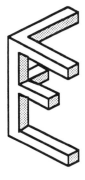

Projections showing views from the top, from the front, etc., are often used to represent geometric solids in a plane. A figure as seen from the front is called a front view, and a figure as seen from above is called a top view.

The following example shows projections of a triangular prism.

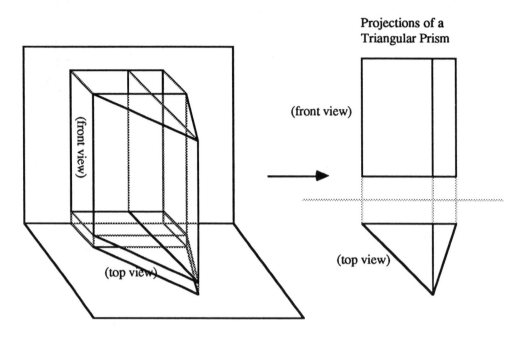

Projections of a
Triangular Prism

(front view)

(top view)

Problem 4   Which of the following geometric solids are expressed in projections
(1)–(4): rectangular parallelepiped, triangular prism, quadrangular
pyramid, cylinder, cone, sphere?

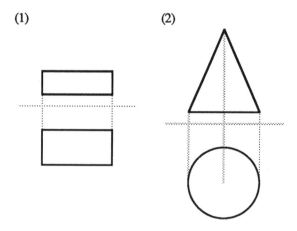

(1)

(2)

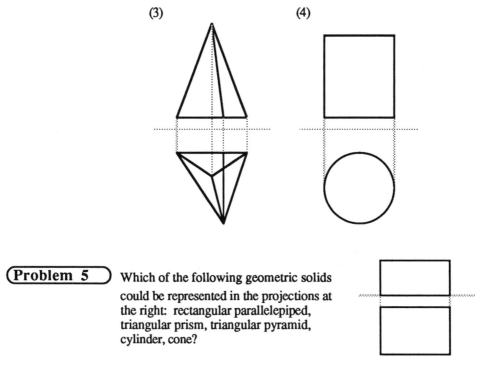

(3)   (4)

Which of the following geometric solids could be represented in the projections at the right: rectangular parallelepiped, triangular prism, triangular pyramid, cylinder, cone?

As we saw in Problem 5, when we draw projections consisting of only a front view and a top view, it is not easy to recognize the shape of a geometric solid. Therefore we add a figure of the view seen from the side, as shown below.

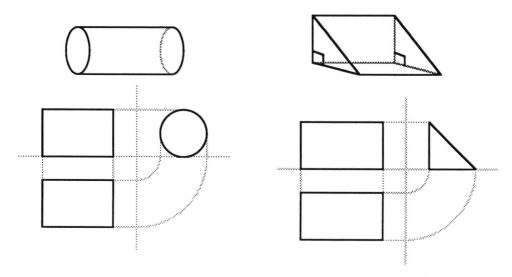

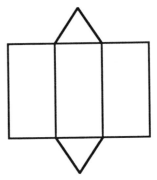

In order to represent geometric solids in a plane, we may use nets, in addition to sketches and projections. The figure at the right is a net of a triangular prism. A net is made by first opening the surfaces of a geometric solid by cutting appropriate lines and then drawing the opened form on a plane. That area is the surface area of the geometric solid.

Problem 6   The figure at the right is a net of a regular tetrahedron. Assuming we can use the net to construct a regular tetrahedron, answer the following questions.

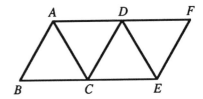

(1) Which edge will coincide with edge *AB*?

(2) Which edge is skew with respect to edge *AB*?

Problem 7   Nets cannot always be drawn for all geometric solids. Give examples of geometric solids for which nets cannot be drawn.

Sections of Geometric Solids

When we cut geometric solids with a plane, the sections have different forms depending on how they are cut.

In the figure below (b) and (c) are sections formed by cutting the rectangular parallelepiped shown in (a) with a plane. In (b) the section is a parallelogram, and in (c) it is a hexagon.

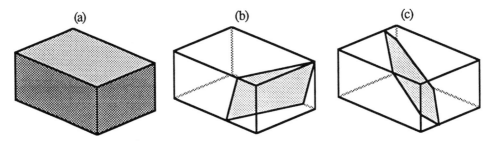

(a)   (b)   (c)

Problem 8 When we cut a rectangular parallelepiped with a plane, is it possible for the section to be a triangle?

Problem 9 How must we cut a rectangular parallelepiped in order for the section to be a rectangle?

Problem 10 In the following diagrams when a cube is cut by a plane containing vertices *B* and *D*, the section is either a triangle or a trapezoid.

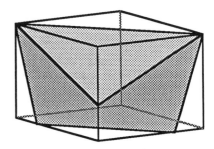

(1) What kind of figure will the section be if we cut it with a plane that contains vertices *B*, *D*, and *G*?

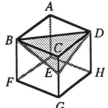

(2) How must we cut the cube with a plane containing the vertices *B* and *D* so that the section will be a rectangle?

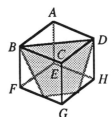

The diagram at the right shows a regular quadrangular pyramid cut by plane *P*, which contains vertex *A* and the midpoints *M* and *N* of edges *BC* and *DE*, respectively.

In this instance, the section is an isosceles triangle. Furthermore, edges *BC* and *DE* are perpendicular to plane *P*, and they are divided into two equal parts by plane *P*.

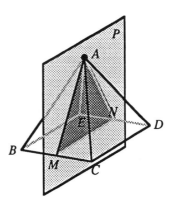

Problem 11 If the regular quadrangular pyramid above were cut by a plane
containing vertices *A*, *B*, and *D*, what form would the section have?

If we cut this pyramid with a plane parallel to base *BCDE*, what form would the
section have?

Exercises

1. Sketch the geometric solid formed by
    revolving the shaded area of the figure at the
    right about line *l* as an axis.

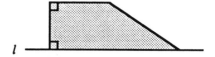

2. The diagram at the right is a sketch of a geometric
    solid formed by cutting a prism having an equilateral
    triangle as its base with a plane parallel to one of the
    lateral faces. Using this information, answer the
    following questions.

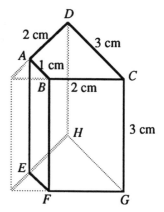

    (1) Which surface is parallel to edge *AE*?

    (2) What is the total number of edges that are skew
         with respect to edge *BC*?

    (3) What form will the section have if we cut this
         geometric solid with a plane that contains
         edge *EH* and vertex *C*?

3. Draw a net of the geometric solid in the sketch in 2.

SURFACE AREA AND VOLUME OF GEOMETRIC SOLIDS

 Prisms and Cylinders

If we designate the length, width, and height (or altitude) of a rectangular parallelepiped as a, b, and c, respectively, then the volume V can be expressed as

$$V = abc.$$

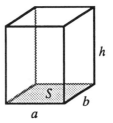

Since a rectangular parallelepiped is a quadrangular prism with a rectangle as its base, if we designate the two sides of the base as a and b and the height as h, we can express the volume V as

$$V = abh.$$

Since ab is the area of the base, we can set ab equal to S and arrive at

$$V = Sh.$$

Generally, the volume of any prism or cylinder can be found by

(area of the base) × (altitude).

If we let the area of the base be S and the altitude be h, then the volume V of a cylinder and/or a prism can be expressed by the following equation:

$$V = Sh$$

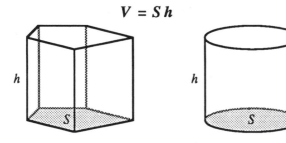

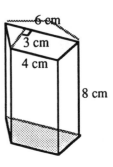

Problem 1   We have a quadrangular prism whose base is a trapezoid. The altitude of this prism is 8 cm, and the upper base, lower base, and height of the base trapezoid are 4 cm, 6 cm, and 3 cm, respectively. Find the volume of the prism.

Problem 2   We have a triangular prism whose base is a right triangle. The altitude of this triangular prism is 7 cm, the sides of the base which form the right angle of the triangle are 3 cm and 4 cm, and the remaining side is 5 cm. Find:
(1)   the base area   (2)   the lateral area
(3)   the total area   (4)   the volume

Note: The base area means the area of one base, and the lateral area means the total area of all the lateral faces.

Problem 3   If the perimeter of a base of a prism is l, the altitude is h, and the lateral area is A, how can you write an expression for A?

If r is the radius of the base of a cylinder and S is the base area, then, since

$$S = \pi r^2$$

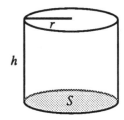

the formula for the volume V of a cylinder of altitude h can be expressed as

$$V = \pi r^2 h.$$

Problem 4   Find the volume of a cylinder if the radius of the base is 5 cm and the altitude is 30 cm.

The net of a cylinder is formed from a rectangle and two circles in the following way. From this representation we can find the lateral area and total surface area of a cylinder.

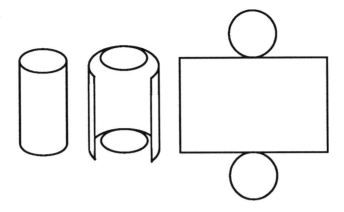

Problem 5 Find the lateral area and the total area of the cylinder in Problem 4.

Problem 6 Write a formula for the lateral area of a cylinder whose altitude is h and whose base radius is r. Write a formula for the total area.

Problem 7 Find the ratio of the volumes of two cylinders formed when rectangle $ABCD$, where $AB = 5$ cm and $BC = 3$ cm, is revolved about the axes formed by sides AB and BC, respectively. Then, find the ratio of their total areas.

2 Pyramids, Cones, and Spheres

If we fill a cone-shaped container with water and pour this water into a cylinder whose base area and altitude are the same as the cone's, we discover that the depth of the water in the cylinder is exactly $\frac{1}{3}$ of the altitude of the cone.

A cube can be broken into three rectangular pyramids with the same size and shape, as shown in the figure at the top of the next page.

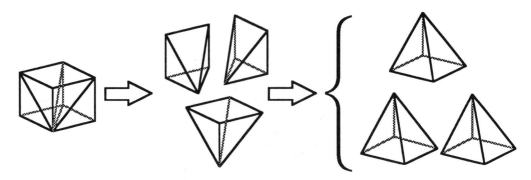

Generally, the volume of a pyramid or a cone is equal to $\frac{1}{3}$ of the volume of a prism or a cylinder with the same altitude and the same base area.

Thus, if the base area of a pyramid is S and the altitude is h, the volume V can be expressed by the following formula:

$$V = \frac{1}{3} S h$$

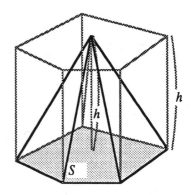

Problem 1 Find the volumes of the pyramids below.

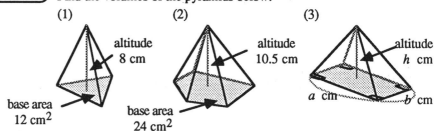

(1)
altitude
8 cm

base area
12 cm^2

(2)
altitude
10.5 cm

base area
24 cm^2

(3)
altitude
h cm

a cm b cm

In the case of a cone, if the radius of the base is r, then the area of the base S is πr^2. Therefore, we can derive the following formula to find its volume V:

$$V = \frac{1}{3} \pi r^2 h$$

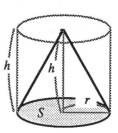

(Problem 2) Find the volume of a cone with base radius 5 cm and altitude 9 cm.

A net of a cone consists of a sector made from the lateral face and a circle made from the base. The length of the arc of this sector is equal to the circumference of the base.

  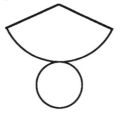

(Example 1) The figure below and at the right is a net of a cone. Find the central angle of sector OAB.

[Solution] Since the length of arc AB is equal to the circumference of circle O',

$$\overset{\frown}{AB} = 2 \times \pi \times 2 = 4\pi \text{ (cm)}$$

The arc length of the sector is proportional to the central angle, so if the central angle is $x°$, then

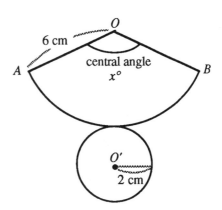

$$x = 360 \times \frac{(\text{length of } \overset{\frown}{AB})}{(\text{the circumference of circle } O)}$$
$$= 360 \times \frac{4\pi}{12\pi}$$
$$= 360 \times \frac{1}{3} = 120$$

Answer: 120°

(Problem 3) Find the lateral area of the cone shown in the net in Example 1.

(Problem 4) Find the total area of a cone with base radius of 3 cm and generatrix of 5 cm.

It is known that the volume of a sphere is $\frac{2}{3}$ of the volume of a cylinder in which the sphere can fit exactly. We can confirm this using a cylindrical receptacle into which a sphere fits perfectly.

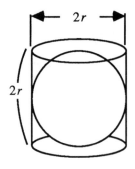

If r designates the radius of the sphere, then the volume of the cylinder in the figure above is equal to $2\pi r^3$. Then the volume of the sphere V can be expressed as $2\pi r^3 \times \frac{2}{3}$, or

$$V = \frac{4}{3} \pi r^3$$

It is also known that the surface area of a sphere is equal to the lateral area of a cylinder into which the sphere can fit exactly. If we let the radius of the sphere be r, then the lateral area of the cylinder equals $4\pi r^2$. Therefore, the surface area S of the sphere will be

$$S = 4\pi r^2$$

(Problem 5) Find the surface area and volume of a sphere of radius 2 cm.

Exercises

1. The shaded figure at the right combines a square and a sector. Find the volume and the total area of the solid of revolution formed by revolving this shaded figure about the axis of line l.

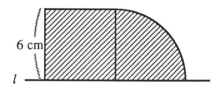

6 cm

l

2. The cube at the right has an edge of 6 cm.
    Solve the following problems.

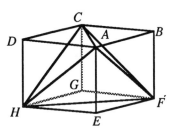

    (1)   Find the volume of the triangular
          pyramid *AHEF*.

    (2)   Using the answer to (1), find the volume
          of the triangular pyramid *AHFC*.

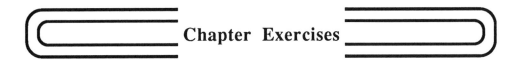

Chapter Exercises

A

1. The figure at the right is a prism with a right
    triangle as its base.

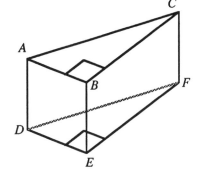

    (1)   Which edges are parallel to *AD*?

    (2)   Which edges are parallel to plane *DEF*?

    (3)   Which edges are perpendicular to plane
          DEF?

    (4)   Which faces are perpendicular to plane
          ADEB?

    (5)   Which edges are skew with respect to
          line *AD*?

2. The diagrams to the right are projections of the
    geometric solid formed by cutting a regular
    parallelepiped with one plane. Given this information,
    do the following problems.

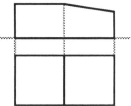

    (1)   Make a sketch of this geometric solid.

    (2)   What kind of polyhedron is this solid?

3. Draw a net of a regular square pyramid in which a side of the base is 3 cm and the
    length of the lateral edge is 5 cm.

4. Find the volume and the total area of the
   following solids:

   (1) The regular square pyramid at the right.

   (2) A sphere of radius 6 cm.

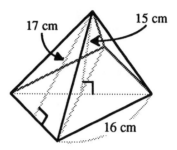

5. Find the base area, the lateral area, and the total area of a cone with a base radius of
   9 cm and a slant height of 15 cm.

B

1. Answer the following questions about the cube shown
   in the diagram at the right.

   (1) Which face is parallel to *CF*?

   (2) How many faces are skew with respect to *CF*?

   (3) If we cut this cube with a plane parallel to plane
       CDEF, what kind of figure will the section be?

   (4) Which is the shortest distance around the surface
       of the cube from point *M*, the midpoint of
       side *AD*, to vertex *F* which passes through a
       point on edge *AE*? Draw a net and show this.

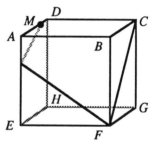

2. The figure at the right shows a
   triangular pyramid. Draw a net of this
   triangular pyramid. Also, find the
   volume of this solid.

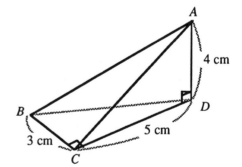

3. The diagram at the right shows a geometric solid formed by cutting a corner of a cube with a plane. Find the volume of this solid.

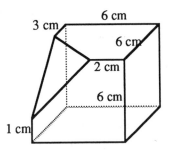

4. Find the volume and the total area of the pipe shown in the diagram at the right. Also, find the volume and the surface area of a sphere that can fit perfectly into this pipe.

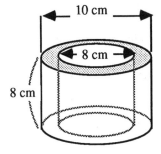

164

Computation Exercises

1. Calculate the following:

    (1)   49 + 53   (2)   62 − 46

    (3)   24 x 7   (4)   57 x 41

    (5)   0 ÷ 25   (6)   852 ÷ 6

2. Calculate the following expressions. For the division problems, divide until there are no remainders.

    (1)   53.2 + 42.6   (2)   2.63 + 0.485

    (3)   4.62 − 0.85   (4)   50.4 − 9.38

    (5)   1.7 x 0.8   (6)   2.58 x 6.05

    (7)   5.25 ÷ 75   (8)   7.05 ÷ 4.7

3. In the following division problems, find the integer quotients and write the remainder, if there is one.

    (1)   703 ÷ 37   (2)   438 ÷ 18

    (3)   150.9 ÷ 6.7   (4)   60.02 ÷ 4.35

4. In the following division problems, find the quotients by rounding off to two decimal places.

    (1)   13.07 ÷ 6   (2)   6.457 ÷ 0.8

    (3)   0.5842 ÷ 0.253   (4)   0.925 ÷ 4.9

5. Calculate the following:

    (1) $\frac{1}{7} + \frac{3}{7}$ (2) $\frac{3}{5} + \frac{3}{5}$

    (3) $2\frac{1}{8} + 3\frac{5}{8}$ (4) $\frac{9}{11} - \frac{3}{11}$

    (5) $\frac{9}{10} - \frac{1}{10}$ (6) $3\frac{1}{9} - 2\frac{5}{9}$

    (7) $\frac{2}{5} + \frac{4}{5} - \frac{3}{5}$ (8) $\frac{7}{12} - \frac{1}{12} + \frac{5}{12}$

6. Calculate the following:

(1) 49 + 87 + 13

(2) 87 x 20 x 5

(3) 24 x 8 + 16 x 8

(4) 67 x 4 – 17 x 4

(5) 314 x 7 + 314 x 3

(6) 900 ÷ 25 + 4

(7) 35 + 5 x 3

(8) 60 – 40 ÷ 5

(9) 28 + 4 – 3 x 1

(10) 78 – 18 x 3 + 27

(11) 30 – (21 + 6) + (33 – 24)

(12) 100 – {(8 + (15 – 52 + 4)}

7. Calculate the following:

(1) $\frac{1}{2} + \frac{2}{3}$

(2) $\frac{3}{4} + \frac{5}{6}$

(3) $3\frac{9}{20} + 9\frac{4}{5}$

(4) $\frac{4}{5} - \frac{3}{10}$

(5) $\frac{7}{8} - \frac{5}{12}$

(6) $2\frac{5}{12} - 1\frac{3}{4}$

(7) $\frac{5}{6} - \frac{3}{4} + \frac{1}{3}$

(8) $1\frac{4}{5} - \frac{2}{3} - \frac{5}{6}$

8. Calculate the following:

(1) $\frac{5}{6} \times 3$

(2) $\frac{1}{4} \times \frac{5}{6}$

(3) $3\frac{1}{4} \times 2\frac{2}{5}$

(4) $\frac{6}{7} \div 3$

(5) $\frac{5}{6} \div \frac{2}{7}$

(6) $6\frac{2}{3} \div 3\frac{3}{4}$

(7) $\frac{1}{6} \times 1\frac{4}{11} \times 2\frac{1}{5}$

(8) $2\frac{6}{7} \times \frac{24}{25} \div 1\frac{1}{3}$

9. Calculate the following:

(1) $3.5 + \frac{3}{4}$

(2) $3\frac{3}{5} - 0.75$

(3) $\frac{3}{8} \times 7.5$

(4) $6.4 \div 2\frac{2}{3}$

(5) $\left(\frac{2}{3} + \frac{1}{2}\right) \times \frac{5}{28}$

(6) $2\frac{1}{6} - 1\frac{3}{4} + 1\frac{2}{5}$

2

1. Factor the following numbers into their primes and find all of the divisors.

    (1)   39   (2)   48   (3)   63   (4)   105

2. Find the greatest common divisor and the least common multiple for the following numbers:

    (1)   7,   15   (2)   12,   15

    (3)   144,   108   (4)   12,   30,   42

3. Calculate the following:

    (1) $+ 27$ (2) $- \ 6$
         $+) \quad + \ 8$ $+) \quad - \ 59$

    (3) $(+25) + (-25)$ (4) $(-3.9) + (+5.1)$

    (5) $\left(-\frac{1}{2}\right) + \left(+\frac{2}{3}\right)$ (6) $0 - (- \ 17)$

    (7) $+ 31$ (8) $- 39$
         $-) \quad - \ 27$ $-) \quad - \ 47$

    (9) $(-0.5) - (+3.3)$ (10) $\left(-\frac{1}{4}\right) - \left(+\frac{2}{5}\right)$

4. Calculate the following:

    (1) $(-20) \times (+18)$ (2) $0 \times (-15)$

    (3) $(-0.8) \times (-0.5)$ (4) $(-80) + (+16)$

    (5) $(-1.9) + (-3.8)$ (6) $\left(-2\frac{1}{2}\right) + \left(+4\frac{1}{3}\right)$

5. Calculate the following:

    (1) $13 + (-12) - (-6)$

    (2) $-7 - (-6) - 4$

    (3) $3 - 7 + 2$

    (4) $-3 + 5 - 16$

    (5) $10 - 6 \times 3$

    (6) $6 - 8 \times (-4)$

    (7) $(-7 + 2) \times 3$

    (8) $12 - (-24) + 6$

    (9) $4^2 - 5 \times 3$

    (10) $3 \times 2^2 + 5$

    (11) $(-7) \times (-3)^2$

    (12) $-2^2 \times 3 - (-6)^2$

6. Calculate the following:

    (1) $(-24) \times 3 + (-9)$

    (2) $(-0.42) + 0.21 \times (-0.35)$

    (3) $\{3 - (12 - 7)\} \times 5$

    (4) $(-4) \times \{0.4 + (-2.4)\}$

    (5) $18 + (-2)^2 \times (-2^2)$

    (6) $2^2 + (-1)^3 + 3 \times (-1)^2$

7. Find the value of the following expressions for $a = -3$ and $b = 4$.

    (1) $-a^2$

    (2) $2a^2$

    (3) $-0.6b$

    (4) $3a + 2b$

    (5) $-8ab$

    (6) $\dfrac{a}{3} + \dfrac{b}{2}$

    (7) $a^2 + b^2$

    (8) $a^2 + ab - b^2$

8. Calculate the following:

    (1) $3x + 5x$

    (2) $-7a + a$

    (3) $-x - 4x$

    (4) $\dfrac{4}{3}a - \dfrac{1}{2}a$

    (5) $6x - 4 - 5x + 3$

    (6) $-m + 1 - \dfrac{m}{3} - \dfrac{1}{2}$

    (7) $(5x + 4) + (x - 7)$

    (8) $(-3x + 5) + (2x - 9)$

    (9) $(6x - 3) - (4x - 5)$

    (10) $(8 - 6y) - (3 - y)$

    (11) $2(x - 3) + 4(2x - 1)$

    (12) $-5(x - 4) + 2(x + 6)$

    (13) $3(x - 7) - 2(x + 3)$

    (14) $7(2x - 1) - 6(5 - 3x)$

    (15) $\dfrac{5}{2}x \times 8 + \dfrac{x - 3}{4} \times 8$

    (16) $(x - 2) - \dfrac{3x + 7}{2} \times 6$

9. Solve the following equations:

(1) $x + 8 = -3$

(2) $-x + 9 = -5$

(3) $8x = 24$

(4) $-2x = 7$

(5) $2x + 1 = 7$

(6) $3x - 10 = x$

(7) $2x + 5 = 5x - 16$

(8) $3x - 4 = 8x - 14$

(9) $7 - 9x = 2x - 15$

(10) $8 - (x + 2) = 5$

(11) $3x = 8 - 2(7 - 2x)$

(12) $2(x - 1) + 3 = 12x - 19$

10. Solve the following equations:

(1) $2.5x - 3 = 1.3x + 1.8$

(2) $0.8 - 0.09x = 0.2x - 0.07$

(3) $\frac{x}{6} + \frac{x}{2} = 8$

(4) $\frac{1}{4}y - \frac{1}{8}y = 6$

(5) $\frac{1}{6}(x - 3) = \frac{x}{5} - 2$

(6) $\frac{3t + 2}{5} = \frac{4t - 1}{3}$

3

1. Calculate the following:

(1) $\frac{1}{3} + \frac{1}{4} - 0.5$

(2) $\frac{1}{3} - \frac{2}{3} \times 0.6$

(3) $(-2)^3 + \frac{4}{5}$

(4) $\frac{5}{12} + \frac{1}{3} \times (-2)^2$

(5) $(-2)^3 + \left(-\frac{2}{3}\right)^2$

(6) $\left(-\frac{8}{9}\right) \times \frac{1}{12} + \left(-\frac{2}{3}\right)^2$

2. Find the value of each of the following expressions for $x = 1, x = \frac{1}{3}$, and $x = -2$.

(1) $x^2 - 2x - 1$

(2) $2x^2 - x + 1$

(3) $\frac{12}{x}$

(4) $\frac{x}{3} + \frac{3}{x}$

3. Calculate the following:

(1) $x - \dfrac{1}{3}(x - 1)$

(2) $\dfrac{1}{4}(2x - 3) - x$

(3) $\dfrac{3x - 2}{2} \times 6 + \dfrac{4x - 3}{3} \times 6$

(4) $\dfrac{a + 4}{3} \times 12 - \dfrac{a - 3}{4} \times 12$

(5) $\left(\dfrac{5a - 4}{3} - \dfrac{a - 2}{6} \right) \times 6$

(6) $\left(\dfrac{2m - 3}{3} - \dfrac{m - 4}{4} \right) \times 12$

4. Solve the following equations:

(1) $x - \dfrac{x - 1}{2} = 2x - 1$

(2) $0.5x - \dfrac{1}{3}(4 - x) = 1$

(3) $\dfrac{4x - 1}{3} + \dfrac{2x}{5} = 6\dfrac{3}{5}$

(4) $4(x - 1) = \dfrac{5x - 1}{3} + 2x$

(5) $1.3x - 1.2(x - 1.5) = 1.5$

(6) $7 - \dfrac{x - 1}{2} = \dfrac{3}{4}(5x - 7)$

Review Exercises

1. Integers

1. Solve the following problems.

   (1) How many multiples of 7 are there among the integers from 1 to 50?

   (2) If we divide 50 by a certain integer, the remainder will be 8. Find all such integers.

   (3) If we divide 73 by a certain integer, the remainder will be 7. Find the smallest such integer.

   (4) Find all those integers which can be divided into both 52 and 112 with a remainder of 4.

2. Factor the following numbers into primes and express them using exponents.

   (1) 96　　　　　　(2) 150　　　　　　(3) 360

3. Factor the following numbers into primes. Using the results, indicate which integers have the following numbers as their squares.

   (1) 64　　　　　　(2) 196　　　　　　(3) 576

4. Answer the following questions with respect to two-digit integers.

   (1) How many different two-digit integers are there all together?

   (2) How many of these numbers are evenly divisible by 8?

   (3) How many of these numbers are evenly divisible by 12?

   (4) How many of these numbers are evenly divisible by both 8 and 12?

5. A rectangular piece of land is 52 m wide and 72 m long. We want to plant trees along the perimeter at equal intervals. If we want to plant a tree at each of the four corners and keep the number of trees as small as possible, how many meters apart should we plant trees? How many trees will we need?

2. Positive and Negative Numbers

1. Find the following numbers:

    (1) The number that is -8 greater than 5.

    (2) The number that is 8 greater than -7.

    (3) The number that is -4 less than -5.

    (4) The number that is -4 less than 0.

2. Solve the following problems.

    (1) Which is the greatest of the following numbers?

    $$-0.01, \qquad -0.1, \qquad -1, \qquad 0$$

    (2) Which is the smallest of the following numbers?

    $$-0.3, \qquad -\frac{1}{3} \qquad -\frac{11}{37} \qquad -\frac{7}{22}$$

    (3) If you add 7 to a certain integer, the result is a positive number, but if you add 5 to it, the result is a negative number. Find this integer.

    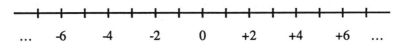

    $$\ldots \quad -6 \quad -4 \quad -2 \quad 0 \quad +2 \quad +4 \quad +6 \quad \ldots$$

    (4) Write in increasing order the integers whose absolute value is smaller than 7 and larger than 4.

3. After recording the temperature every two hours on a winter day, we produced the chart below. What is the average of these temperatures?

time	0:00	2	4	6	8	10	12	14	16	18	20	22
temp.(°C)	-3.7	-4.5	-5.6	-6.3	-4.0	5.8	11.5	12.2	9.1	4.9	3.0	0.4

Find the average of the temperatures at 6:00, 14:00, and 22:00, and compare this average with the average you found above.

4. We are given two numbers, a and b, and a is a positive number and b is a negative number. Answer the following questions:

    (1) Which is larger, $a + b$ or $a - b$?

    (2) Which is larger, $a - b$ or $a - 2b$?

3. Letters and Expressions

1. Simplify the following expressions:

   (1) $a \times (-1)$

   (2) $6 \times \frac{1}{3} y$

   (3) $(-8a) + 6$

   (4) $(x - y) + a$

   (5) $a + (x - y)$

   (6) $a \times b \times a \times b \times a$

   (7) $a \times 5 - 3 \times b$

   (8) $a + b + (-2)$

   (9) $a \times (a + 1) \times (a + 1)$

   (10) $x + (y + 3) \times 2$

2. Write an expression for each of the following quantities:

   (1) The product of b and the sum of a and 3.

   (2) The remainder when you divide a pencils among 25 students, giving each student x pencils.

   (3) The positive integer in which the hundreds place, the tens place and the ones place are represented, respectively, by the letters a, b, and c.

   (4) The original number of articles if a articles are placed in each box, and the pth box still has space left for r articles.

   (5) The selling price when the original price a of an article has been reduced by p percent.

   (6) The distance traveled at a speed of v km/hour for a minutes.

   (7) The average score in a game when player m has x points and player n has y points.

3. In the figure at the right, write an expression showing the area of the shaded portion of the rectangle, in which a parallelogram-shaped section has been removed.

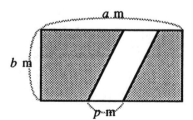

4. Given two numbers a and b, answer the following questions.

   (1) When $-5a < 0$, is a a positive or a negative number?

   (2) When $2b < 0$, is b a positive or a negative number?

   (3) Is the product ab of a in (1) and b in (2) a positive or a negative number?

4. Equations

1. Indicate with an equality the relations between the following quantities.

    (1) $\frac{3}{4}$ of x is exactly 7 larger than 3 times y.

    (2) The cost of a half dozen pencils costing a yen each and 3 notepads costing b yen each is 500 yen.

    (3) A group of students is collecting money to buy a souvenir. They are 25 yen short when they collect a yen from each of x students, and b yen short when they collect 30 yen from each student.

    (4) To reach a certain spot 15 km away we can spend x minutes riding a bus at 30 km/hour or we can walk at a speed of 4 km/hour for y hours.

    (5) There were x students in elementary school last year. This year there are 750 students, a $p\%$ increase over last year.

2. In the following equations, when the value of x is the number given in brackets [ ], find the value of a so that the equations are true.

    (1) $5x + a = 3x + 6$ [5]

    (2) $4 - 5(a - 2x) = -a + 2x$ [-3]

3. Find the following numbers by writing equations.

    (1) The number which is the same when it is tripled as when 3 is added to it.

    (2) The number which is the same when divided by 4 as when 4 is subtracted from it.

    (3) The number which is the same when multiplied by 5 as when 5 is subtracted from it.

    (4) The number which is the same when divided by 10 as when 10 is added to it.

4. When graduating seniors were being seated at graduation, three people were put on each bench, but then there were 25 people who could not be seated. When four people were put on each bench, there were exactly 4 benches remaining. How many graduates were there?

5. An express train that passed through station A at 48 km/hour had to slow down to 32 km/hour because of deep snow 30 minutes after passing through station A. It then reached station B 30 minutes behind schedule. How many kilometers apart are station A and station B?

5. Functions and Proportions

1. y is proportional to x, and if $x = 6$, then $y = 3$. Express y in terms of x.

2. y is proportional to x, and if $x = 8$, then $y = 15$. What is the value of x for $y = 16$?

3. For (a)–(f) below:

    (1) Express y in terms of x.

    (2) State in which cases y is proportional to x and in which cases y is inversely proportional to x. In each case, indicate the constant of proportionality.

    (a) One article costs 5 yen, and x articles cost y yen.

    (b) The perimeter of a rectangle x cm long and 3 cm wide.

    (c) The area of a parallelogram with a base of x cm and height of y cm is 24 cm^2.

    (d) When x cm of a 17.5 cm pencil is used, the remaining length is y cm.

    (e) While the minute hand of a watch moves $x°$, the hour hand moves $y°$.

    (f) If you travel 48 km at a rate of x km/hour, it takes y hours.

4. If manuscript paper contains 600 characters per page and there are x characters per line and y lines per page, solve the following problems.

    (1) Express y in terms of x.

    (2) If the number of characters it takes to fill one line is $20 \le x \le 28$, how would you determine the values of both x and y?

5. On a number line, x and y are the numbers that express two points symmetrical with respect to the point 5. Given this information, solve the following problems.

    (1) Find the value of y for $x = 7$.

    (2) Find the value of y for $x = -3$.

    (3) Express y in terms of x.

6. Plane Figures

1. Four points $A, B, C,$ and D, are arranged in this order in one straight line such that

$$AB = BD, \quad BC = CD.$$

Use expressions to describe the relation between the lengths of the following segments:

(1) AB and BC (2) AB and AD (3) AD and CD

2. Extend segment AB, which is 6 cm long, beyond B, and mark a point C such that $BC = 4$ cm. If we designate the midpoint of segment AC as M and the midpoint of segment BC as N, find the lengths of segments $AM, AN,$ and MN.

3. The figure at the right depicts a sector with a central angle of 90°, and a semicircle. Find the perimeter and the area of the shaded part.

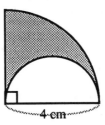

4-cm

4. Using a ruler and compass,

   (1) Construct segment AB and construct the circle of which this segment is the diameter.

   (2) Construct $\angle AOB$ of 180°, and then construct ray OC so that $\angle BOC$ equals $\frac{1}{3}$ of $\angle AOC$.

5. In the figure at the right, we are given a line l and a point A at a distance of 3 cm from l. What is the total number of points that satisfy both of the following conditions (a) and (b)?

   (a) The distance from A is 5 cm.

   (b) The distance from l is 1 cm.

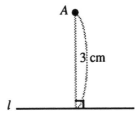

7. Figures in Space

1. Answer the following questions about the rectangular parallelepiped at the right.

    (1) Which edge is perpendicular to line *EG*?

    (2) What is the total number of edges that are skew with respect to line *EG*?

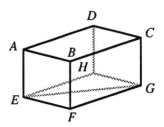

2. At the right are a diagram and partial projection of a geometric solid formed by joining two cylinders. Solve the following problems.

    (1) Find the total area and volume of the solid.

    (2) Add the missing part of the projection.

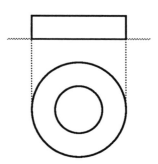

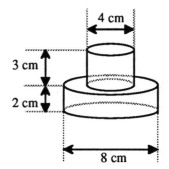

3. In the diagram at the right, find the volume of the solid formed by revolving the shaded portion about line XY.

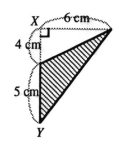

4. In the figure at the right, a cone of radius 9 cm is revolving on a plane. It takes $2\frac{1}{2}$ revolutions of the cone to form one complete circumference of the circle described by the pale line.

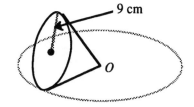

   (1) Find the slant height of this cone.

   (2) Find the total area of this cone.

Answers to Computation Exercises and Review Exercises

Computation Exercises

1

1. (1) 102   (2) 16
   (3) 168   (4) 2337
   (5) 0   (6) 142

2. (1) 95.8   (2) 3.115
   (3) 3.77   (4) 41.02
   (5) 1.36   (6) 15.609
   (7) 0.07   (8) 1.5

3. (1) 19
   (2) 24, remainder 6
   (3) 22, remainder 3.5
   (4) 13, remainder 3.47

4. (1) 2.18   (2) 8.07
   (3) 2.31   (4) 0.19

5. (1) $\dfrac{4}{7}$ (2) $1\dfrac{1}{5}$
   (3) $5\dfrac{3}{4}$ (4) $\dfrac{6}{11}$
   (5) $\dfrac{4}{5}$ (6) $\dfrac{5}{9}$
   (7) $\dfrac{3}{5}$ (8) $\dfrac{11}{12}$

6. (1) 149   (2) 8700
   (3) 320   (4) 200
   (5) 3140   (6) 9
   (7) 50   (8) 52
   (9) 4   (10) 51
   (11) 27   (12) 90

7. (1) $1\dfrac{1}{6}$ (2) $1\dfrac{7}{12}$
   (3) $13\dfrac{1}{4}$ (4) $\dfrac{1}{2}$
   (5) $\dfrac{11}{24}$ (6) $\dfrac{2}{3}$
   (7) $\dfrac{5}{12}$ (8) $\dfrac{3}{10}$

8. (1) $2\dfrac{1}{2}$ (2) $\dfrac{5}{24}$
   (3) $7\dfrac{4}{5}$ (4) $\dfrac{2}{7}$
   (5) $2\dfrac{11}{12}$ (6) $1\dfrac{7}{9}$
   (7) $\dfrac{1}{2}$ (8) $2\dfrac{2}{35}$

9. (1) $4\dfrac{1}{4}$ (2) $2\dfrac{17}{20}$
   (3) $2\dfrac{13}{16}$ (4) $2\dfrac{2}{5}$
   (5) $\dfrac{5}{24}$ (6) $\dfrac{11}{12}$

2

1. (1) 3×13; 1, 3, 13, 39
   (2) $2^4 \times 3$; 1, 2, 3, 4, 6, 8, 12, 16, 24, 48
   (3) $3^2 \times 7$; 1, 3, 7, 9, 21, 63
   (4) $3 \times 5 \times 7$; 1, 3, 5, 7, 15, 21, 35, 105

2. greatest common divisor, least common multiple, respectively
   (1) 1, 105   (2) 3, 60
   (3) 36, 432   (4) 6, 420

3. (1) 35   (2) -65
   (3) 0   (4) 1.2
   (5) $\dfrac{1}{6}$ (6) 17
   (7) 58   (8) 8
   (9) -3.8   (10) $-\dfrac{13}{20}$

4. (1) -360   (2) 0
   (3) 0.4   (4) -5
   (5) 0.5   (6) $-\dfrac{15}{26}$

5.   (1)   7   (2)   -5
     (3)   -2   (4)   -14
     (5)   -8   (6)   38
     (7)   -15   (8)   16
     (9)   1   (10)   17
     (11)   -63   (12)   -48

6.   (1)   8   (2)   0.7
     (3)   -10   (4)   8
     (5)   2   (6)   6

7.   (1)   -9   (2)   18
     (3)   -2.4   (4)   -1
     (5)   96   (6)   1
     (7)   25   (8)   -19

8.   (1) $8x$ (2) $-6a$
     (3) $-5x$ (4) $\frac{5}{6}a$
     (5) $x-1$ (6) $-\frac{4}{3}m+\frac{1}{2}$
     (7) $6x-3$ (8) $-x-4$
     (9) $2x+2$ (10) $-5y+5$
     (11) $10x-10$ (12) $-3x+32$
     (13) $x-27$ (14) $32x-37$
     (15) $22x-6$ (16) $-8x-23$

9.   (1) $x=-11$ (2) $x=14$
     (3) $x=3$ (4) $x=-\frac{7}{2}$
     (5) $x=3$ (6) $x=5$
     (7) $x=7$ (8) $x=2$
     (9) $x=2$ (10) $x=1$
     (11) $x=6$ (12) $x=2$

10. (1) $x=4$ (2) $x=3$
     (3) $x=12$ (4) $y=48$
     (5) $x=45$ (6) $t=1$

3

1.   (1) $\frac{1}{12}$ (2) $-\frac{1}{15}$
     (3)   -10   (4)   5
     (5)   -18   (6) $-\frac{1}{6}$

2.   for $x=1$
     (1)   -2   (2)   2

     (3)   12   (4) $\frac{10}{3}$
     for $x=\frac{1}{3}$
     (1) $-\frac{14}{9}$ (2) $\frac{8}{9}$
     (3)   36   (4) $\frac{82}{9}$
     for $x=-2$
     (1)   7   (2)   11
     (3)   -6   (4) $-\frac{13}{6}$

3.   (1) $\frac{2}{3}x+\frac{1}{3}$ (2) $-\frac{1}{2}x-\frac{3}{4}$
     (3) $17x-12$ (4) $a+25$
     (5) $9a-6$ (6) $5m$

4.   (1) $x=1$ (2) $x=\frac{14}{5}$
     (3) $x=4$ (4) $x=11$
     (5) $x=-3$ (6) $x=3$

Review Exercises

1. Integers

1.   (1)   7   (2)   14, 21, 42
     (3)   11   (4)   6, 12

2.   (1) $2^5 \times 3$ (2) $2 \times 3 \times 5^2$
     (3) $2^3 \times 3^2 \times 5$

3.   (1) $64 = 2^6 = 8^2$
     (2) $196 = 2^2 \times 7^2 = 14^2$
     (3) $576 = 2^6 \times 3^2 = 24^2$

4.   (1)   90   (2)   11
     (3)   8   (4)   4

5.   every 4m, 62 trees

2. Positive and Negative Numbers

1.   (1)   -3   (2)   1
     (3)   -1   (4)   4

2   (1)   0   (2) $-\dfrac{1}{3}$

     (3)   -6   (4)   -6, -5, 5, 6

3.   average temperature 1.9°C;
the average temperature at 6:00,
14:00, 22:00 is 2.1°C, and it is
0.2°C higher

4.   (1) $a-b$ (2) $a-2b$

3. Letters and Expressions

1.   (1) $-a$ (2) $2y$

     (3) $-\dfrac{4}{3}a$ (4) $\dfrac{x-y}{a}$

     (5) $\dfrac{a}{x-y}$ (6) a^3b^2

     (7) $5a-3b$ (8) $-\dfrac{a}{2b}$

     (9) $a(a+1)^2$ (10) $\dfrac{2x}{y+3}$

2.   (1) $(a+3)b$ (2) $(a-25x)$
     (3) $100a+10b+c$
     (4) $(ap-r)$
     (5) $\left(a-\dfrac{ap}{10}\right)$ yen

        or $a\left(1-\dfrac{p}{10}\right)$ yen

     (6) $\dfrac{50av}{3}$ m or $\dfrac{av}{60}$ km

     (7) $\dfrac{mx+ny}{m+n}$ points

3. $(ab-bp)$ m²

4.   (1)   positive   (2)   negative
     (3)   negative

4. Equations

1.   (1) $\dfrac{3}{4}x = 3y+7$

     (2) $6a+3b=500$
     (3) $ax-25=30x+b$

     (4) $\dfrac{x}{2}+4y=15$

     (5) $x\left(1+\dfrac{p}{100}\right)=750$

2.   (1) $a=-4$ (2) $a=-5$

3.   (1) $\dfrac{3}{2}$ (2) $\dfrac{16}{3}$

     (3) $-\dfrac{5}{4}$ (4) $-\dfrac{100}{9}$

4.   148

5.   72 km

5. Functions and Proportions

1. $y = \dfrac{1}{2}x$

2   $x = \dfrac{15}{2}$

3.   (1)   (a) $y = 5x$
         (b) $y = 2x+6$
         (c) $y = \dfrac{24}{x}$
         (d) $y = 17.5-x$
         (e) $y = \dfrac{1}{12}x$
         (f) $y = \dfrac{48}{x}$

     (2)   proportions (a), (e); inverse
proportions (c), (f);
the constant of proportionality
expresses
(a) the price of one article
(c) the area of the
       parallelogram
(e) the angle of the hour
       hand when the minute
       hand moves 1°
(f) the total distance

4.   (1) $y = \dfrac{600}{x}$
     (2)   for $x=20$ $y=30$
         for $x=24$ $y=25$
         for $x=25$ $y=24$

5.   (1) $y=3$ (2) $y=13$
     (3) $y=-x+10$

6. Plane Figures

1. (1) $AB = 2BC$
    (2) $2AB = AD$
    (3) $AD = 4CD$

2. $AM = 5$cm, $AN = 8$cm
    $MN = 3$ cm

3. perimeter: $(4\pi + 4)$ cm
    area: 2π cm^2

4. (1)

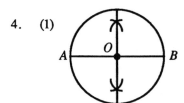

    (2)

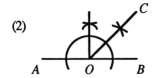

5. 4

7. Figures in Space

1. (1) AE, CG (2) 6

2. (1) volume: 44π cm^3
            total area: 60π cm^2
    (2) see the diagram below

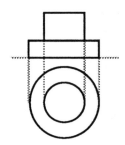

3. 60π cm^3

4. (1) $22\frac{1}{2}$ cm

    (2) $283\frac{1}{2}\pi$ cm^2

182

Index

Art and Photo Acknowledgments

UCSMP gratefully acknowledges the photographs and numerous illustrations taken from the original Japanese textbook *New Mathematics 1* and used here with the kind permission of the Japanese publisher, Tokyo Shoseki Company, Ltd. UCSMP would also like to thank Mr. Shigeki Ohyama of Tokyo Shoseki for his help in obtaining the following photographs: page 76, © Tetsuo Abe; page 96, © The Meteorological Agency. UCSMP is grateful to Mr. Joseph A. Swojenski of the First National Bank of Chicago and Mr. Ed Nash of the Illinois Department of Transportation for providing the photographs on page 137.

Various Sections of a Rectangular Parallelepiped

直方体のいろいろな切り口

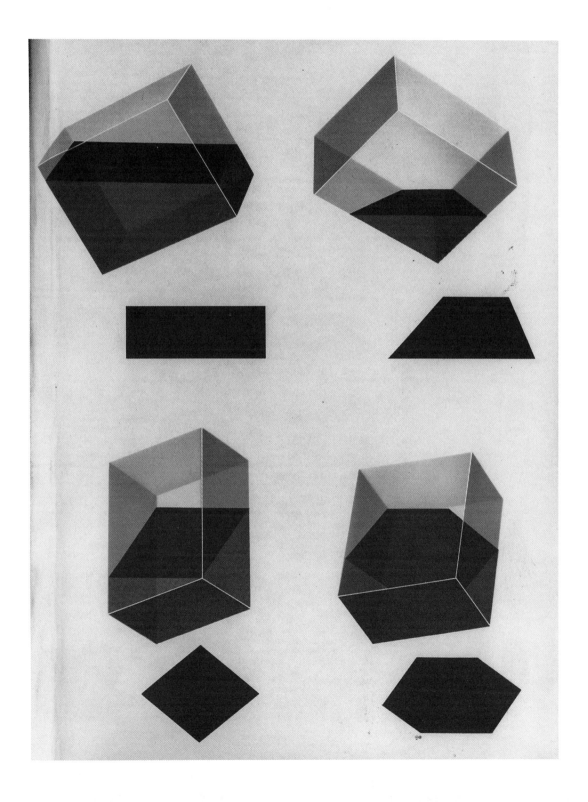